PRACTICAL ALARM

Other Titles of Interest

PRACTICAL ALARM
PROJECTS

by

R. A. PENFOLD

**BERNARD BABANI (publishing) LTD
THE GRAMPIANS
SHEPHERDS BUSH ROAD
LONDON W6 7NF
ENGLAND**

Please Note

Although every care has been taken with the production of this book to ensure that any projects, designs, modifications and/or programs, etc., contained herewith, operate in a correct and safe manner and also that any components specified are normally available in Great Britain, the Publishers do not accept responsibility in any way for the failure, including fault in design, of any project, design, modification or program to work correctly or to cause damage to any other equipment that it may be connected to or used in conjunction with, or in respect of any other damage or injury that may be so caused, nor do the Publishers accept responsibility in any way for the failure to obtain specified components.

Notice is also given that if equipment that is still under warranty is modified in any way or used or connected with home-built equipment then that warranty may be void.

First Published – June 1997

British Library Cataloguing in Publication Data

A catalogue record for this book is available from the British Library

ISBN 0 85934 416 9

Cover designed by Gregor Arthur

Printed and bound in Great Britain by Cox & Wyman Ltd, Reading

Preface

It is not that long ago that most burglar alarms contained nothing more advanced than switches, wire, and an electrically operated bell. The vast majority of alarms were fitted to commercial premises, and there were very few domestic installations. With advances in technology and a rising crime-rate all this has changed. Burglar alarm systems have become quite hi-tech, and they are commonly installed in flats, houses, cars, boats, and just about anything that can be broken into. Switches of one type or another are still the most common form of sensor for burglar alarms, but there are now a variety of sophisticated detectors that can be used to back-up traditional window and door switches. These include passive infra-red, active infra-red, and ultrasonic sensors.

Burglar alarm systems are something that can easily be built at low cost by the home constructor. Chapter 1 of this book provides details of two switch activated alarms, together with an audio alarm and power supply circuits. A portable alarm for use with bags and cases containing valuables is also included. Chapter 2 deals with higher-tech circuits, such as fibre-optic loop alarms, and advanced sensors for the switch activated alarms. These include passive infra-red and ultrasonic sensors, a Doppler shift ultrasonic movement detector, and a twin beam infra-red sensor.

Stripboard layouts and wiring diagrams are provided for all the circuits. Plenty of notes on construction and full components lists are also included. Most of the circuits are therefore suitable for those who have little or no experience of electronic project construction.

R. A. Penfold

Contents

Chapter 2 (Continued)

Chapter 1

SWITCH BASED ALARMS

I suppose that security alarms are rather like insurance, in that you pay for them in the hope that it is a waste of money, and they will never be needed! In truth, most alarms are probably never put to the "acid test", but this does not mean they are a waste of time and money. Even if an alarm system is never used in earnest, it can provide its owner with great peace of mind. Also, an alarm system can act as a deterrent, and the fact that it is installed reduces the risk of the protected premises ever being burgled.

Switch activated alarms are probably the most common type, and are certainly the most simple type of intruder alarm. Although very simple and low-tech, they are still very effective provided the sensor switches are properly installed. This book is primarily concerned with the electronic side of things rather than the installation of sensor switches. Nevertheless, it is worth considering some of the basics of switch type sensors. These days they are usually supplied complete with leaflets which give a lot of useful advice about their installation, and it is clearly advisable to carefully study any leaflets of this type. The manufacturers instruction leaflets give installation advice that is specific to their version of a particular switch. The advice given here has to be of a more general nature.

Which Type?
There are two main types of sensor switch, which are the micro and reed varieties. A micro-switch is basically just an ordinary switch mechanism, which may or may not be housed in a case of some sort. Whether of open or closed construction, a micro-switch does not have any form of control knob for manual operation. A micro-switch is intended for automatic operation, and in security applications it is normally operated when a door or window is opened and closed. This type of switch varies somewhat in its exact form, but there is usually a small lever which sticks out from the body, and the switch changes position when this lever is pressed towards the body.

1

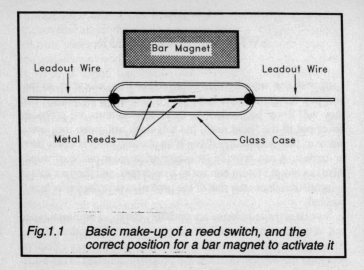

Fig.1.1   *Basic make-up of a reed switch, and the*
             correct position for a bar magnet to activate it

A reed switch is operated by a magnet, and it takes the basic form shown in Figure 1.1. It consists of what is usually a hermetically sealed glass encapsulation (but is sometimes plastic these days), plus two metal reeds. The reeds are simply very thin pieces of springy metal which are mounted so that their ends overlap slightly. These act as the switch contacts. The ends of the reeds are very close together, but they do not actually touch. Accordingly, there is no electrical contact between them. If a bar magnet is placed in the position shown in Figure 1.1 it produces mutual attraction between the two reeds, which then touch and close the switch. There is no longer any mutual attraction if the magnet is removed, and the reeds then spring apart and open the switch. Note that a reed switch can only be activated by a bar magnet in the position shown in Figure 1.1. A "horseshoe" magnet will not operate a reed switch, and neither will a bar magnet if one end or the other is placed next to the switch.

   Both types of switch will operate reliably in security applications if they are installed correctly, or will give poor results if they are not. In the past I have tended to prefer reed switches, which were generally a little more expensive, but somewhat easier to install. These days there is no difficulty in obtaining

2

various reed switches that are specifically intended for security applications. The available types include simple surface mounting magnets and switches, types which are recessed into the door or window and its frame, and self-adhesive switches and magnets for use with uPVC windows and doors. It is worth noting that drilling into recently installed windows, particularly µPVC types, often invalidates the long term guarantee. Life will be a lot easier if you use reed switches specifically designed for use in security applications, rather than improvising using reed or micro-switches that are not.

Surface mounting switches are the easiest type to use, and they are simply screwed or glued in place, depending on the type of windows and doors fitted to the premises. It is just a matter of fitting the reed switch to the frame, and the magnet to the door or window. It is possible to do things the other way round, but it is much easier if the switch and the wiring to it are fitted on the fixed frame rather than the moving door or window. The switch and magnet are positioned where they will be side-by-side when the door or window is closed.

This means that the switch contacts will normally be closed, and that they will open when the door or window is opened. Most alarm systems will operate with switches that close when activated, or switches that open when activated, or a combination of the two. Normally closed switches are generally considered to be the better type, since cutting the wires to this type of switch will activate the alarm. Cutting the wires to normally open switches disables them.

Recessed switches offer a somewhat neater solution, with the magnets and switches fitted largely out of sight within the doors, windows, and frames. Fitting them is obviously a bit more time consuming, and requires rather more skill. Also, this type of switch and magnet is normally only applicable to wooden doors, windows and frames. They are used in the same basic manner as the surface mounting variety, giving normally closed contacts which open when the door or window is opened.

Foiling Intruders
Windows can be protected using strips of self-adhesive metal foil. This is normally used around the edges of windows, and

there is electrical continuity through the foil giving a form of normally closed switch. Special terminals are available which make it easy to produce reliable connections to the strips of foil. The idea of this type of sensor is that it will be activated if the intruder enters by breaking the glass, rather than forcing the window open. Even a crack in the window beneath the foil is normally sufficient to sever the foil, produce an open circuit, and trigger the alarm. Obviously the foil must be fitted on the inside of the window where a would-be intruder can not tamper with it.

The only other common type of switch sensor is the switch mat, which is also known as a pressure mat. These are normally positioned out of sight under carpets or rugs. If anyone steps on a pressure mat it results in a short circuit being placed across the two leads fitted to it. Unlike other types of sensor switch, pressure mats are therefore of the normally open variety. They are mainly used as a back-up to door and window switches, but they can act as the only sensors if you do not want unsightly switches and wiring going to all the windows and doors in the building. Switch mats must be position where they stand a good chance of being activated by burglars. This usually means in front of opening windows, in doorways, or in front of drawers, cupboards, etc., where valuables are kept.

Most alarms now have at least one "panic switch", which is simply a switch that is manually operated to trigger the alarm system. This is only needed when the alarm is used with the premises occupied, which normally means at night when everyone is asleep. The idea is that if an intruder should get into the premises without triggering the alarm, but someone should hear the intruder, they can press a "panic switch" to activate the alarm and (hopefully) scare off the intruder.

The panic switch could be an ordinary non-locking push-button type wired in with the other sensor switches. It could be a normally open or normally closed type, provided it is wired into the sensor switches in the appropriate manner. However, with an alarm that has a delay before the alarm is activated, it might be better to use a locking push-to-make switch wired across the relay contacts that control the alarm generator. This ensures that the alarm sounds as soon as the switch is operated, and that the intruder is scared away as soon as possible.

4

Basic Alarm

A practical alarm circuit normally has the ability to operate with any number of normally open and (or) normally closed sensor switches. There is no difficulty in using large numbers of switches of either type, and it is just a matter of wiring them in the appropriate fashion. Normally open switches are wired in parallel, as shown in Figure 1.2. The normally closed variety are wired in series, as shown in Figure 1.3.

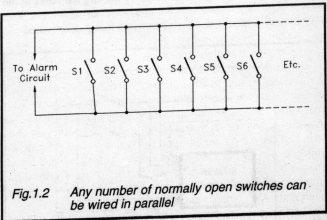

Fig.1.2 *Any number of normally open switches can be wired in parallel*

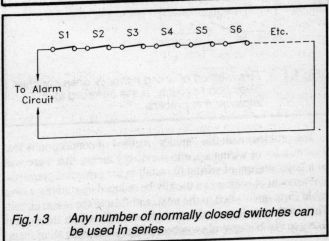

Fig.1.3 *Any number of normally closed switches can be used in series*

With normally open switches there is a definite advantage in having individual inputs for each sensor on the alarm circuit. Cutting a wire to one of the switches then leaves the others fully operational. In practice there are few (if any) alarm circuits that have more than one pair of input terminals for normally open switches. It is still possible to have the switches operating largely independently of each other if the switches are wired in the manner illustrated in Figure 1.4. All the switches can still be deactivated simultaneously, but only by cutting the wires at the point where they connect to the alarm circuit. Cutting a wire anywhere else results in only one switch being deactivated.

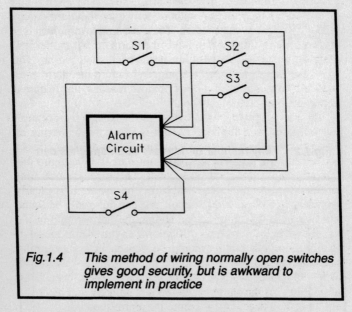

Fig.1.4   *This method of wiring normally open switches gives good security, but is awkward to implement in practice*

The problem with this "spider" method of connection is that it takes a lot of wiring up, and inevitably means that there will be a large amount of wiring to install in the protected premises. The amount of wiring can usually be reduced by running a twin cable from one switch to the next, and then to the alarm circuit. This method is less secure though, and a break in the wire is likely to disable several switches, and could disable all of them!

Normally closed switches are the easier to install, since it is just a matter of running a single wire from the alarm circuit to the first switch, then to the second switch, and so on. The circuit is completed by running a wire from the final switch to the other input terminal of the alarm circuit. As pointed out previously, cutting the wire at any point results in the alarm being activated.

Delays

Practical alarm circuits often include a couple of delay circuits which enable the user to get into and out of the protected premises without activating the alarm. The first problem is how to get out of the building without activating the alarm circuit that you have just switched on. The most simple approach is to have a built-in timer which holds the alarm circuit in the "off" state for about 30 seconds after it has been switched on. This gives the user time to exit the premises before the alarm automatically switches itself on. For obvious reasons, this feature is generally known as an exit delay.

The second problem is how to get back into the premises without activating the alarm. This is often tackled using an alarm fitted with an entrance delay circuit. In other words, once activated, the alarm generator does not start flashing lights and activating sirens for about 30 seconds. This gives the user time to enter the premises and switch off the alarm. It is clearly necessary to have an alarm circuit that can not easily be found and switched off by an intruder. Hiding the alarm circuit inside a cupboard helps to make it difficult for an intruder to locate it. Ideally the alarm circuit should be housed in a very strong metal case which can not easily be forced open, and the on/off switch should be a good quality key type. Then, even if an intruder locates the alarm generator, it is unlikely that he or she will be able to deactivate it before the alarm sounds.

It is not essential to use exit and entry delays, and there are some good alternatives. The most simple of these is to have the on/off switch located somewhere on the exterior of the building so that you can switch on the alarm after you have left the building, and switch it off again before entering. The obvious drawback of this method is that it leaves the system vulnerable to an intruder who might find the switch and deactivate the

7

alarm. Things can be made difficult for would-be intruders by using a good quality key switch, or (preferably) some form of combination lock.

Greater security is likely to be provided by some form of remote on/off switching. The up-market approach is to use a radio link, and there are licence exempt transmitter and receiver modules that can be used in this application. In my admittedly somewhat limited experience of these modules, they are very easy to use and provide excellent results. Their only major drawback is that they are relatively expensive.

The cheaper alternative is to use an infra-red link. Unlike u.h.f. radio signals, infra-red "light" can not go through walls, doors, or other opaque objects. The receiver therefore has to be positioned behind a window where it can "see" the signal from the transmitter. Another limitation is that the maximum range tends to be comparatively low, and for the most simple systems it is strictly limited. An infra-red remote control is still a very good method where low cost remote switching is required.

Alarm System

The block diagram for a basic switch activated alarm circuit appears in Figure 1.5. The sensor switches connect to a simple logic gate, and the output of this gate goes high if one or more of the sensor switches is activated. However, one input of the gate is fed from a timer circuit, and this holds the output of the gate low for about 30 seconds after switch-on. This timer provides the exit delay.

The output signal from the gate is fed through a lowpass filter. False alarms are a major problem with alarm systems, and these are often caused by electrical noise. This can be in the form of mains-borne noise spikes caused by electrical devices switching on and off, and radiated by the mains supply wiring. Probably the biggest cause of problems though, are powerful noise spikes radiated from lightning. There are usually many metres of wire connecting all the sensor switches to the alarm circuit, and this wiring acts as a very good aerial for receiving noise spikes from lightning and mains cables. The lowpass filtering removes any brief glitches caused by electrical noise, but otherwise allows the system to function normally.

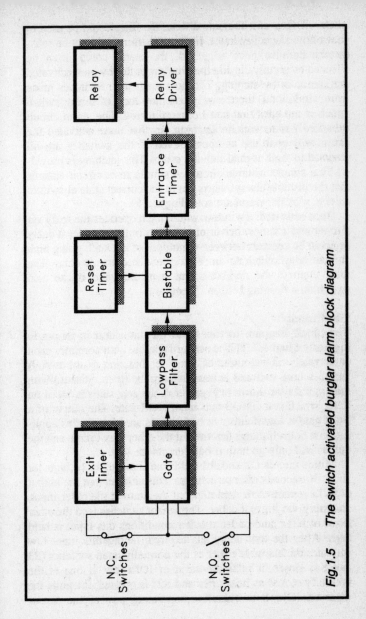

Fig.1.5   The switch activated burglar alarm block diagram

On the face of it the output from the filter could be used to control the alarm generator. In practice this would not be satisfactory because once triggered, the alarm could often be silenced by simply closing the window or door which activated the alarm, or by stepping off the switch mat. Switches made from window foil are the only common form of sensor switch which is not easily reversed once triggered. The alarm circuit therefore has to include latching, so that once activated the alarm will continue to sound, even if the switches are all returned to their normal standby states. This latching is provided by a simply bistable circuit. A simple reset circuit ensures that the bistable always starts out in the correct state at switch-on (i.e. with the alarm not sounding).

Once activated, the output of the latch operates the relay via a timer and a simple driver circuit. The timer provides a delay of about 30 seconds between the output of the latch going high and the relay switching on. This gives the entrance delay. The relay controls the audible alarm generator, and it can also switch on a flashing beacon if required.

The Circuit

The circuit diagram for the basic burglar alarm is shown in Figures 1.6 and 1.7. This alarm will operate with normally open or normally closed switches, or a combination of the two. It includes both exit and entrance delay facilities. Starting with the input stages shown in Figure 1.6, the gate stage is based on IC1a, which is a CMOS two input NOR gate. The output of a NOR gate is low if either or both inputs are high. In this application it helps if things are viewed the other way round, and the output will only go high if both inputs are low.

In this circuit C2 and R2 hold one input of IC1a high for about 30 seconds after switch-on. This ensures that the output of IC1a remains low regardless of the state at the other input, and this gives the exit delay. The sensor switches feed the other input of IC1a, and under standby conditions this input is held high. After the exit delay has expired, taking this input low activates the alarm. If either of the normally open switches (S3 and S4) closes, it pulls the input of IC1a low. If one of the normally closed switches (S1 and S2) is opened, R4 pulls the input of IC1a low. Therefore, operating any of the sensor

10

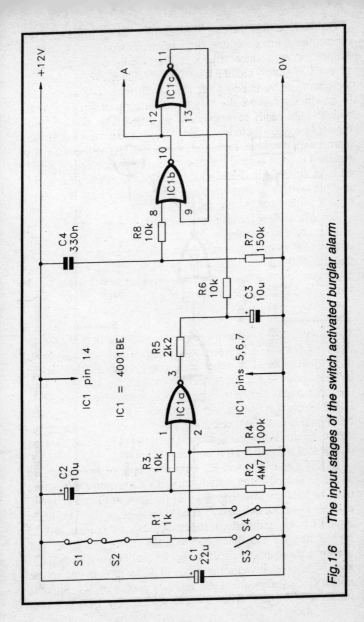

Fig.1.6   The input stages of the switch activated burglar alarm

11

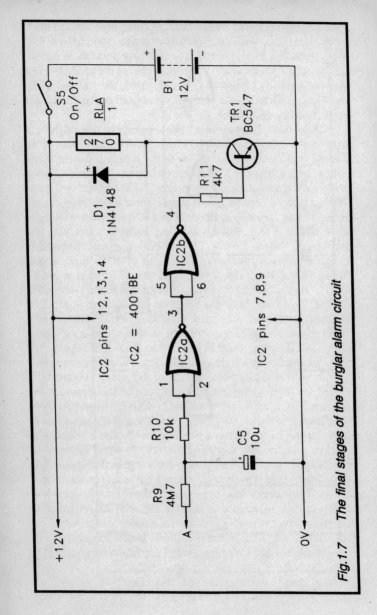

Fig. 1.7   The final stages of the burglar alarm circuit

12

switches results in the output of IC1a going high and the alarm being activated. Although only two sensor switches of each type are shown in Figure 1.6, it is of course possible to use any desired number of switches of either type. In the unlikely event that no normally closed switches are used, the top end of R1 must be connected to the positive supply rail or the circuit will be permanently activated.

IC1 contains four two input NOR gates, but one of these is unused. As usual with a CMOS logic device, the inputs of the unused gate are connected to one of the supply rails (the 0 volt rail) in order to prevent spurious operation. No connection is made to the output of this gate (pin 4). The other two gates (IC1b and IC1c) are used in a simple set/reset bistable circuit, or flip/flop as it is also known. C4 and R7 provide a reset pulse at switch-on which ensures that the bistable starts with the output of IC1b low. Taking pin 13 of IC1c high sets the bistable to the alternative state with the output of IC1b high, and it latches in that state. The output of IC1a is connected to pin 13 of IC1c via a simple C-R lowpass filter circuit comprised of R5 and C3. These filter out any spurious pulses on the output of IC1a that might otherwise cause false alarms. If there are severe problems with noise pickup it might also be necessary to add a 470n filter capacitor from IC1a pin 2 to the 0 volt supply rail, but in most cases this additional filtering will not be required.

Turning now to the output stages of the circuit (Figure 1.7), R9 and C5 form a simple C-R timing circuit that provides the entrance delay. IC2 is another CMOS 4001BE quad two input NOR gate, but in this case only two of the gates are utilized. Each gate has its two inputs wired together so that it operates as a simple inverter, and the two inverters are wired in series to provide what is effectively a non-inverting buffer stage. The point of this stage is to provide a very high input resistance that will not significantly load the entrance timer circuit, but a low enough output impedance to operate the relay driver reliably. The relay driver is a simple common emitter switch based on TR1. D1 is the usual protection diode which suppresses any high reverse voltage spikes generated across the relay coil as it is switched off.

The current consumption of the circuit is around 45 milliamps once the unit is activated, but it is only about

120 microamps under standby conditions. Simple CMOS logic devices have insignificant current consumptions when static, and the only significant current flow under standby conditions is through S1, S2, R1, and R4. The minute standby current consumption makes it practical to run the circuit from a 12 volt battery, such as eight HP7 size cells in a plastic holder. The battery life should be at least a year and would probably be more like two years provided the batteries are a type which has a long "shelf life". If preferred, the unit could be powered from a 12 volt mains power supply unit. This is perhaps a slightly more convenient solution, but in a security application there is some advantage in using battery power. Any discontinuation in the mains supply will not affect the efficacy of the alarm.

Construction

A suitable stripboard layout for the switch activated burglar alarm circuit is shown in Figures 1.8 (component side view) and 1.9 (copper side view). This layout is based on a board which measures 35 holes by 24 copper strips. In most respects construction of this board is quite straightforward, but there are a few points which merit some amplification.

The board is not one of the standard sizes in which stripboard is sold, so it must be trimmed down from a larger piece. It is easily cut to size using a hacksaw or junior hacksaw, but cut along rows of holes rather than trying to cut between rows. The hole spacing of 0.1 inch pitch board is too narrow to permit cutting between the rows. The sawn edges will be a little rough, but are easily filed to a neat finish.

Inevitably, a fair number of link-wires are required. These can be made from 24 s.w.g. (0.56 millimetre diameter) tinned copper wire, or trimmings from the resistor and capacitor lead-out wires might suffice.

The 4001BE used for IC1 and IC2 is a static sensitive device. Consequently, the standard anti-static handling precautions should be observed when dealing with these components. Use holders for both of them, but do not actually plug them into circuit until the unit is otherwise complete. Until that time they should be left in their anti-static packaging, which will probably be either a special form of blister pack, or a piece of conductive foam. Do not touch their pins any more than is

14

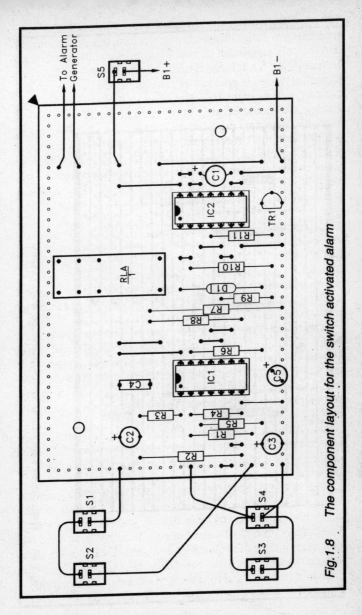

Fig. 1.8   The component layout for the switch activated alarm

15

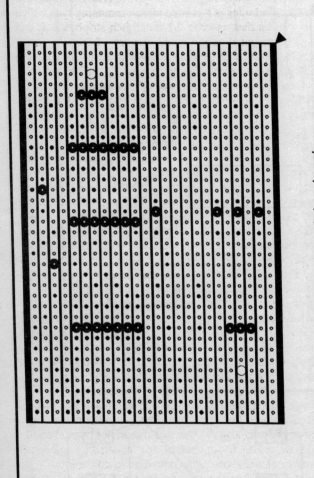

Fig. 1.9   The copper side of the switch activated alarm board

absolutely necessary when fitting them into the holders. Make quite sure that they are fitted with the correct orientation. Getting a CMOS device the wrong way round results in it placing a virtual short circuit on the supply rails. It rapidly heats-up and is soon destroyed if the power is not switched off.

The specified relay is a printed circuit mounting type which has pin spacing that matches 0.1 inch pitch stripboard. It can therefore be mounted on the board like any of the other components. It has single changeover contacts rated at 16A d.c., and 20 amps a.c., at potentials of up to 28 volts d.c. or 240 volts a.c. This should be considerably more than adequate to handle normal alarm generators, beacons, etc. It is advisable to use currents of no more than about five or six amps with stripboard, so for higher current devices the connections would have to be made direct to the terminals of the relay.

Some relays which have the same case and pin configuration as the specified type have twin changeover contacts (with a reduced current rating of 5 amps for each set). For most purposes only one set of contacts will be needed. However, the other set can obviously be utilized if you need to control something like a d.c. alarm generator with one set of contacts, and a 240 volt beacon with another set. The three breaks in the copper strips needed to isolate the two sets of contacts are included Figure 1.9, but these obviously serve no purpose if a single pole relay is used, and they can then be omitted.

Note that the usual safety precautions should be observed if the unit is used to control a mains powered load. In particular, the unit would have to be mounted in a metal case earthed to the mains earth lead. The unit would also have to be housed in a case which would not give easy access to the mains wiring (i.e. one which has a screw fitting lid rather than a clip-on type). In this application it is clearly desirable for the unit to be fitted in a tough case which does not offer easy access, regardless of any safety requirements, but if the unit connects to the mains supply this becomes mandatory. The unit should not be connected to mains powered equipment unless it is installed by someone who is suitably experienced and competent to do the job.

It is not essential to use the specified relay, and any type which has a 12 volt coil with a resistance of about 200 ohms or more, together with suitable contacts, should be satisfactory.

17

The only problem with alternative relays is that they are almost certain to have a different pin arrangement, and will not fit directly into this stripboard layout. Instead, the relay would have to be mounted on the case and then hard wired to the circuit board. Most modern relays are designed for printed circuit mounting, and have no built-in means of case or chassis mounting. In most cases though, they can be fixed to the inside of a case if they are mounted up-side-down, and glued in place using a high quality adhesive. A "superglue" or an epoxy adhesive should give good results.

Figure 1.8 shows only two sensor switches of each type, but any number of switches can be used with the methods of connection described previously. The exit and entrance delays are approximately 30 seconds each, but note that they can not be set with a high degree of accuracy. If either or both delays are up to a few seconds out, this does not indicate a fault, and is the result of normal component tolerances. If the delays are greatly extended, or never actually end, this probably indicates that the timing capacitors have excessive leakage currents. The circuit will only work properly if C2 and C5 are high quality components. Tantalum "bead" capacitors are probably the best type to use, but the prototype worked well using high quality electrolytic capacitors.

Altering the durations of the two delays is very easy. The length of the exit delay is proportional to the value of C2, and the length of the entry delay is proportional to the value of C5. To double the exit delay to 60 seconds, the value of C2 would have to be doubled to 20μ. In practice the nearest preferred value of 22μ would have to be used. To reduce the entrance delay to 20 seconds would require the value of C5 to be reduced by one-third, which works out at just over 3μ1. In practice the nearest preferred value of 3μ3 would be used.

Components for Figures 1.6 and 1.7

Resistors (all 0.25 watt 5% carbon film)
R1	1k
R2	4M7
R3	10k

R4	100k
R5	2k2
R6	10k
R7	150k
R8	10k
R9	4M7
R10	10k
R11	4k7

Capacitors

C1	22µ 16V radial elect
C2	10µ 25V radial elect
C3	10µ 25V radial elect
C4	330n polyester
C5	10µ 25V radial elect

Semiconductors

IC1	4001BE
IC2	4001BE
TR1	BC547
D1	1N4148

Miscellaneous

S1, S2	Normally closed sensor switches
S3, S4	Normally open sensor switches
S5	SPST key switch
B1	12 volt (8 × HP7 cells in plastic holder)
RLA/1	12 volt 270 ohm coil, SPDT 16A contacts (Maplin "12V 16A relay", Cat No. YX99H, or similar, see text)

Strong metal case, 0.1 inch pitch stripboard measuring 35 holes by 24 copper strips, 14-pin d.i.l. holder (2 off), battery connector (PP3 type), wire, solder, etc.

Remote Controlled Alarm

This alarm circuit is a switch operated type, and it is basically the same as the one featured previously. However, the entry and exit delays have been replaced by an infra-red remote control facility. This enables the alarm to be switched on and off from outside the protected premises. Strictly speaking, the alarm is still switched on and off via a key-switch fitted on the case of the alarm, and the remote control is actually controlling an inhibitor circuit which prevents the alarm from being activated. The practical effect is much the same though, with the user "arming" the alarm after leaving the premises, and deactivating it before re-entering.

An infra-red remote control has the advantage of being relatively cheap, but has the obvious disadvantage that it can not be used through doors, walls, or anything that is opaque. The transmitter has to be aimed at the receiver through a window. If necessary, the system can be made quite sensitive so that it will provide good range when used through a window and a medium density lace curtain. Through a window alone it is possible to achieve a range in excess of 10 metres, but through lace curtains a maximum operating range of around 2 to 5 metres is more likely. This is clearly more than adequate, and even a range of a metre or two through fairly "heavy" net curtains should be workable.

System Operation

The block diagram of Figure 1.10 shows the basic arrangement used in this alarm. The sensor switches, gate, bistable, and relay driver stages are much the same as the ones in the alarm circuit described previously. In this case there is no need for an entrance delay circuit between the bistable and the relay driver. Also, the hold-off at the input of the gate circuit is provided by the remote control circuit, and not via an exit timer circuit.

On the face of it, the remote control system could be based on a non-modulated infra-red source and a simple infra-red level detector circuit. In practice such an arrangement does not work very well because the output from the transmitter's infra-red l.e.d. is quite weak. It tends to be swamped by the background infra-red level at ranges of more than about half a metre. Much better range and reliability are obtained if the transmitter pulses the infra-red l.e.d. The exact operating frequency is not important, and in this case it is around 2.5kHz. The point of using a pulsed signal is that it is easily distinguished from the background infra-red signal, which changes at a relatively slow rate.

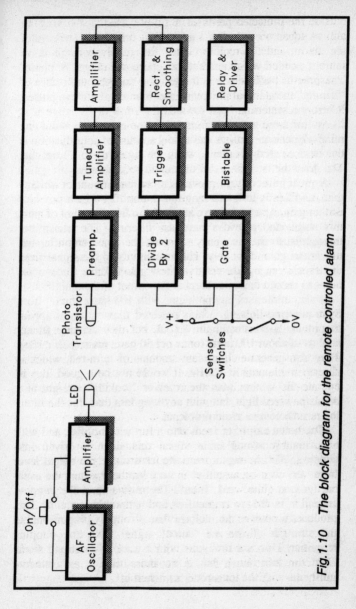

Fig. 1.10 The block diagram for the remote controlled alarm

The transmitter consists of a simple oscillator having an almost squarewave output signal. This drives the l.e.d. via a simple amplifier which provides the relatively high drive current needed to obtain a good operating range. A phototransistor or photo-diode at the receiver converts the pulses of infra-red energy from the transmitter into small voltage pulses. When the system is used towards the limit of its range it is likely that these voltage pulses will be no more than about one millivolt peak-to-peak. A substantial amount of amplification is therefore needed in order to bring the signal up to a level that will drive the later stages of the circuit successfully.

A preamplifier stage provides a certain amount of voltage gain, and this is followed by a tuned amplifier which provides further gain. Apart from providing a substantial amount of gain, this stage also provides bandpass filtering. The transmitter is adjusted to the frequency at which the tuned amplifier has maximum gain. This gives good sensitivity to the signal from the transmitter, but the relatively low gain at other frequencies helps to reduce the noise level at the output of the amplifier.

It also minimises any problems with 100 hertz "hum" from main powered lighting. Mains powered filament bulbs appear to provide a constant light output, but they actually flicker slightly at about 100 hertz (once per 50 hertz mains half cycle). They also generate significant amounts of infra-red, which is slightly modulated at 100Hz. It would not be a good idea to operate the system with the receiver "looking" straight at a mains powered light, but with anything less than this the filtering is sufficient to avoid problems.

The tuned amplifier feeds into a further amplifier, and with a reasonably strong input signal this stage is driven into clipping. With no signal from the transmitter, the output level from the clipping amplifier is very low, and is just the usual background "hiss" and "hum". The output from the clipping amplifier is fed to a rectifier and smoothing circuit. This produces a positive d.c. voltage that is roughly proportional to the strength of the a.c. output signal from the clipping amplifier. This is a few volts with a reasonably strong signal from the transmitter, but is no more than a few hundred millivolts with the transmitter switched off.

The next stage is a trigger circuit, and this produces a high output level if the input voltage is more than about one volt, and a low output level if it is not. This gives a "clean" signal at logic levels which can be used to drive the next stage reliably. This is a simple divide-by-two circuit. Pressing and releasing the on/off switch at the transmitter results in the output of the divide-by-two circuit changing state. Operating the transmitter again switches the output of the divider back to its original state, operating the transmitter a third time results in the output of the divider changing once more, and so on. Each operation of the transmitter toggles the output of the divider. The output of the divider drives an input of the gate circuit, and either activates the alarm or inhibits it, depending on the output state set via the remote control.

In practice the alarm starts out in the inhibited state. After the user has left the protected premises, the transmitter is operated, the output state of the divide-by-two stage is toggled, and the alarm is "armed". Before entering the premises the user operates the transmitter again, and toggles the output of the divider back to its original state so that the alarm circuit is inhibited again.

Transmitter Circuit

The circuit diagram for the transmitter appears in Figure 1.11. This is basically just a standard 555 astable (oscillator) circuit which operates at around two to 2.5kHz. VR1 is adjusted for the operating frequency that gives optimum results. The infra-red l.e.d. (D1) is driven via a simple common emitter switching stage based on TR1. R4 controls the "on" current of D1, and the specified value sets the actual current at about 100 milliamps. The average current is only about 50 milliamps because D1 is switched off for about 50 percent of the time. This is the maximum average current that most five millimetre infra-red l.e.d.s can safely handle.

S1 is the on/off switch, and should obviously be a non-latching pushbutton type. The overall current consumption of the circuit is about 56 milliamps. This is rather a high current consumption for a PP3 size battery, but such a battery is still adequate as the power source because the transmitter will only be switched on briefly and very intermittently. However,

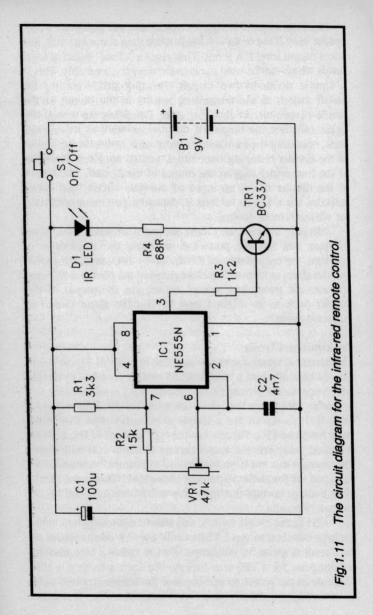

Fig.1.11 The circuit diagram for the infra-red remote control

it is advisable to use some form of "high power" battery if the system is to be used over a long range.

Receiver Circuit

The receiver circuit diagram is shown in Figures 1.12 to 1.14. Taking Figure 1.12 first, this shows the amplifier and trigger stages of the unit. TR1 is a silicon n.p.n. photo-transistor, and in this circuit no connection is made to its base terminal. Under dark conditions TR1 has the very low collector-to-emitter leakage current associated with ordinary silicon transistors. Subjecting TR1 to light, including infra-red "light", results in its leakage current increasing very substantially. The pulses of infra-red "light" from the transmitter therefore generate negative pulses at the collector of TR1.

These are coupled by C3 to the input of the preamplifier, which is a common emitter amplifier based on TR2. Normally a common emitter stage has a very high voltage gain, but in this case the local negative feedback introduced by R5 keeps the voltage gain down to about 16 times. The output of TR2 is coupled to the input of the tuned amplifier by way of C4. The tuned amplifier is another common emitter type, but rather than a resistor it has a parallel tuned circuit (L1 – C5) as its collector load. High voltage gain is achieved at the resonant frequency of the tuned circuit (around two to 2.5kHz), but the voltage gain of the circuit falls away rapidly above and below this frequency.

C6 couples the output of the tuned amplifier to the input of the clipping amplifier. This is based on TR4, and is another common emitter amplifier. Like the preamplifier, the gain of this stage is tamed by the inclusion of an emitter resistor which introduces local negative feedback. Despite this reduced voltage gain, the overall sensitivity of the circuit remains very high, giving good operating range. Where optimum sensitivity is required, R9 can be made lower in value so that the voltage gain of TR4 is increased. However, if the gain of the circuit is made too high, the noise level will be sufficient to hold the output of the trigger stage high, thus preventing the system from working at all.

C7 couples the output of TR4 to a basic half-wave rectifier and smoothing circuit based on D2, D3, and C8. The trigger

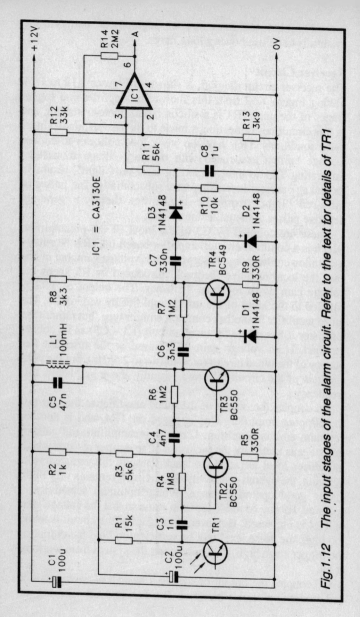

Fig.1.12   The input stages of the alarm circuit. Refer to the text for details of TR1

26

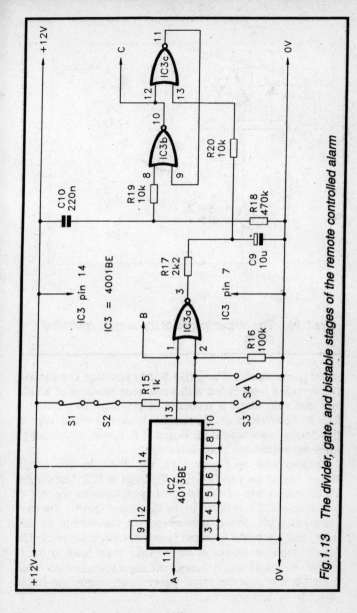

Fig.1.13   The divider, gate, and bistable stages of the remote controlled alarm

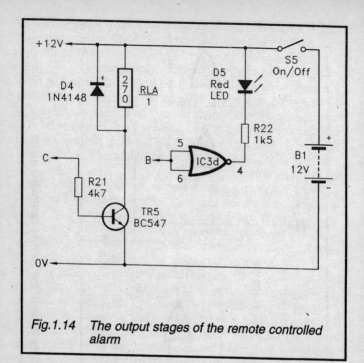

Fig.1.14   The output stages of the remote controlled alarm

circuit uses operational amplifier IC1 as a voltage comparator. The inverting input is fed with a reference potential of a little over one volt, which is produced by potential divider R12 – R13. R14 provides a small amount of hysteresis which helps to give "clean" switching at the output of IC1, with no "jittering" when the switch-over point is reached.

Turning now to Figure 1.13, the divide-by-two circuit utilises one of the two "D" type flip/flops in IC2. The divider circuit makes use of the standard ploy whereby the not Q output (pin 12) is coupled to the data input (pin 9). On each clock pulse the circuit "remembers" the state fed to its data input, and places the Q output (pin 13) at this logic level. The not Q output is always at the opposite logic level to the Q output, and the Q output therefore changes state once per clock cycle. In this case the clock signal is, of course, the output signal from the trigger circuit.

28

The main alarm circuit is based on IC3a to IC3c, and this is basically the same as the alarm circuit described previously. In this circuit the hold-off to pin 1 of IC3a is provided by the output of IC2, rather than by the exit delay circuit.

Figure 1.14 shows the circuit diagram for the relay and relay driver circuit. Again, this is much the same as the equivalent circuit in the alarm described previously. IC3d is wired to act as a simple inverter, and is used to drive l.e.d. indicator D5. D5 switches on when the output of IC2 is high and the alarm is inhibited, and switches off when the output of IC2 is low and the alarm is "armed."

This is really an essential feature, as the user would otherwise not know for certain that the remote control had functioned properly and enabled the alarm. Also, the user might think that the alarm had been deactivated when it had not, and would then set off the alarm on entering the protected building. The remote control circuit is very reliable, but it is important to have a warning if an odd glitch should occur from time to time.

The current consumption of the circuit is about 7 milliamps under standby conditions, and around 40 milliamps higher than this when the relay is switched on. The circuit can be powered from eight HP2 ("D") size cells, and even with several hours use per day each set of batteries should last more than a year. Alternatively, a mains power supply unit can be used, and this represents a very much cheaper method of powering the unit in the long term. The power supply must provide a reasonably stable output voltage, and it must have a low noise level. A suitable mains power supply is described in the next section of this book.

Photocells

D1 can be any five millimetre diameter infra-red l.e.d. intended for use in remote control systems, such as a TIL38 or LD271. L.e.d.s of this type often seem to be sold as something like "5 millimetre infra-red emitter" or "high power infra-red emitter", rather than under a particular type number. You may have a choice of a wide angle or narrow angle type. The narrow angle type produces a tighter but stronger beam of "light". This type is therefore preferable if the system is to be used over a relatively long distance, but the transmitter will have to be aimed at the receiver with a much higher degree of precision.

TR1 in the receiver can be virtually any silicon n.p.n. photo-transistor, but the best type seems to be photo-transistors that have a l.e.d.-like encapsulation. Like l.e.d.s, these are available in five millimetre and three millimetre diameter encapsulations, and the five millimetre variety seems to give by far the best sensitivity. A device such as the BP103B gives good results and is relatively cheap. This type of photo-transistor does not have the base lead accessible, which is of no consequence in the present application, where no connection is made to the base terminal anyway.

Identifying the collector (c) and emitter (e) leads is usually straightforward, with the collector lead being the shorter of the two. Also, the collector lead is usually indicated by a "flat" on the side of the case (Figure 1.15). The base terminal of TR1 is very sensitive to stray pickup, and it should not be connected to the component board if you use a component that does have a base leadout wire. It should be trimmed very short and other-wise ignored.

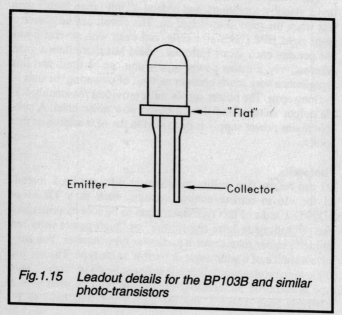

Fig.1.15   Leadout details for the BP103B and similar photo-transistors

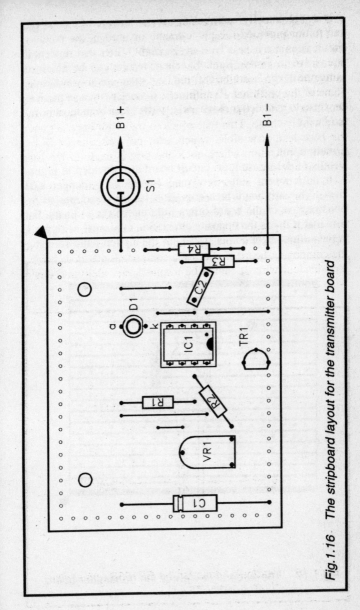

Fig.1.16   The stripboard layout for the transmitter board

It is not actually essential to use an infra-red l.e.d. at the transmitter provided the photo-transistor used in the receiver circuit does not have a built-in "daylight" filter that renders it insensitive to visible light. Excellent results can be obtained using one of the "ultra-bright" red l.e.d.s that are now available. Some of the eight and 10 millimetre diameter types in particular, seem to give better range and a wider beam than most infra-red l.e.d.s.

Construction

Details of the transmitter circuit board are provided in Figure 1.16 (component side view) and Figure 1.17 (copper side view). The stripboard measures 22 holes by 18 copper strips. Construction of the board offers little out of the ordinary, but note that IC1 has the opposite orientation to normal, with pin 1 in the bottom right corner instead of the top left hand corner.

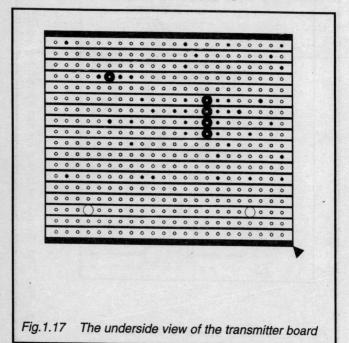

Fig.1.17   The underside view of the transmitter board

32

The transmitter will fit into virtually any small to medium size plastic or metal case. The cathode (k) leadout of D1 will be shorter than the cathode lead. Also, the case normally has a "flat" next to the cathode leadout (Figure 1.18). D1 is shown as being mounted direct on the stripboard panel in Figure 1.16, but it might be easier to mount it in a panel holder and hard wire it to the circuit board. The alternative is to mount D1 on the board and drill a hole in the case for it to "look" through. With this second method it will probably be necessary to leave the lead-out wires of D1 quite long, and to bend them at right angles. The "window" for D1 can then be made in one end of the case, which makes it relatively easy to use the unit and aim it at the receiver with reasonable accuracy. Ideally the hole for D1 should be five millimetres in diameter, and D1 should fit right into it. Bear in mind that using a small "window" and fitting D1 well behind it will make the transmitter very directional, which would make it very difficult to use.

Details of the receiver board are provided in Figures 1.19 to 1.21. Due to the large size of this board (71 holes by 25

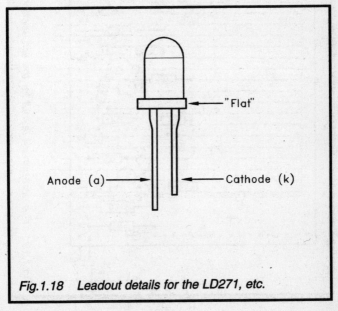

Fig.1.18   Leadout details for the LD271, etc.

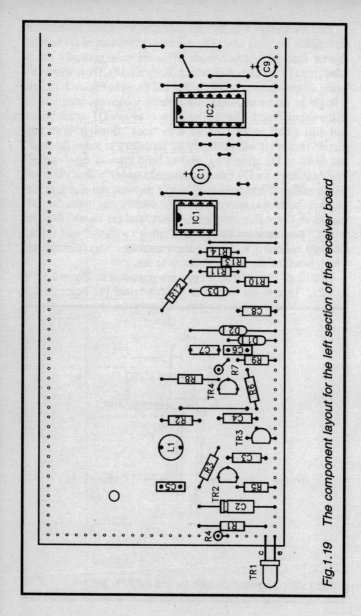

Fig.1.19   The component layout for the left section of the receiver board

34

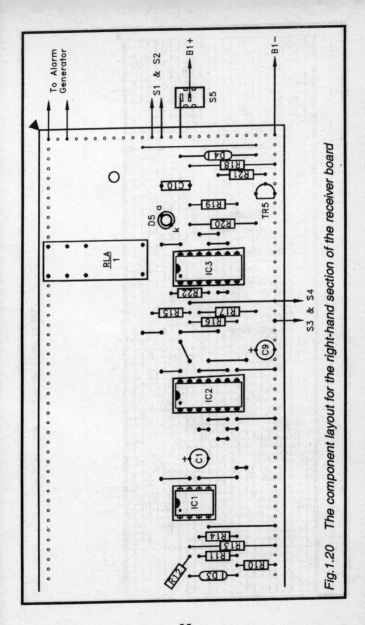

Fig. 1.20 The component layout for the right-hand section of the receiver board

35

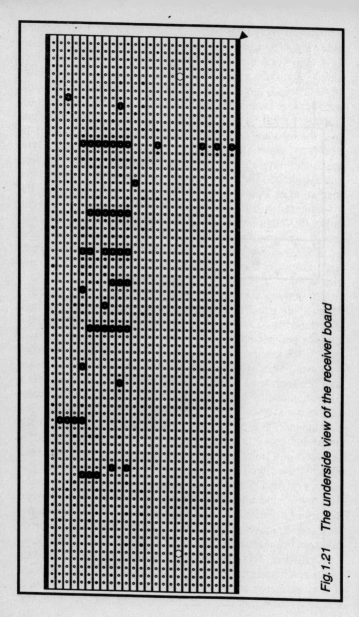

Fig. 1.21   The underside view of the receiver board

36

25 copper strips) it has been necessary to spread the component side view across two drawings (Figures 1.19 and 1.20). There is a considerable overlap between the two drawings which should minimise any inconvenience this causes. Construction of this board is largely straightforward, but as the board is quite complex it is essential to proceed carefully during construction.

Note that all three integrated circuits are CMOS types, and that the standard anti-static handling precautions should be observed when dealing with them. The non-electrolytic capacitors have a mixture of five, 7.5, and 10 millimetre lead spacing. It is difficult to use polyester capacitors which have inappropriate lead spacing, and there is a risk of damaging the components in trying to do so. Rather than trying to obtain polyester components having the appropriate lead spacings, it would probably be easier to use mylar capacitors. These usually have long leads that are easily formed to suit a range of lead spacings. Their quality is more than adequate for this circuit.

The notes about the relay used in the basic switch activated alarm apply equally to the relay in this project. L1 has a high inductance at 100mH, and this could make it difficult to find a suitable component. The inductor used in the prototype is a type 10RB component from Cirkit. The circuit should work well with other inductors having the correct value provided they are intended for use at audio frequencies. There is only a limited amount of space on the circuit board, making it necessary to use an inductor that is also physically quite small.

Although D5 is shown as being mounted direct on the circuit board in Figure 1.20, in practice it will almost certainly have to be fitted in a holder on the front panel of the case, and hard wired to the circuit board. It is advisable to use a high brightness l.e.d. for D5, and I would recommend using something like one of the ultra high brightness eight or 10 millimetre diameter l.e.d.s. This type of l.e.d. has a very high light output level, which makes it easy to see whether D5 is switched on or off, even from some distance away and under bright conditions.

If possible, TR1 should not be mounted off-board, as this could give problems with stray pickup to the connecting lead. If it is necessary to mount it away from the circuit board, a screened connecting lead must be used, and this lead should be kept as short as possible. The outer braiding of the lead carries the connection from the emitter, and the inner conductor carries the connection from the collector. It is better if TR1 is mounted on the board, with a "window" for it being made at a suitable position in the front panel of the case.

Testing, Testing

Start with VR1 in the transmitter at a roughly middle setting. Note that the relay in the receiver may be activated if the alarm is switched on with one of the sensor switches activated. Assuming that the sensor switches are all in the standby state, the relay should not be activated when the alarm is switched on. The divide-by-two circuit could start with D5 switched on or off, but will almost certainly start with D5 switched on. This means that the alarm is in its inhibited mode, but aiming the transmitter at TR1 in the receiver and operating the transmitter's on/off switch a few times should result in D5 switching on and off.

With D5 switched on it should not be possible to trigger the alarm, but with D5 switched off the alarm generator should be activated immediately when the alarm is triggered. Once the alarm generator is sounding it is not possible to silence it by using the transmitter to switch D5 on again. Once triggered the alarm can only be reset by switching off using S5, and then switching the unit back on again a few seconds later.

In theory, by adjusting VR1 it should be possible to maximise the range of the system, but in reality the effect of VR1 seems to be quite small. However, if the system is to be used over a fairly long operating range it is worthwhile experimenting with a range of settings for VR1 in order to find the one that gives optimum results.

Components for Figure 1.11
(Transmitter)

Resistors (all 0.25 watt 5% carbon film)

R1	3k3
R2	15k
R3	1k2
R4	68R

Potentiometer
VR1   47k min hor preset

Capacitors
C1   100μ 10V axial elect
C2   4n7 polyester

Semiconductors
IC1   NE555N
TR1   BC337
D1   LD271 or similar 5mm infra-red l.e.d.
                    (see text)

Miscellaneous
S1   Push-to-make, release-to-break pushbutton
                    switch
B1   9 volt (high power PP3)

Small plastic or metal case, 0.1 inch pitch stripboard having 22
holes by 18 copper strips, 8-pin DIL holder, battery connector,
wire, solder, etc.

Components for Figures 1.12, 1.13 and 1.14
(Receiver)

Resistors (all 0.25 watt 5% carbon film)
R1   15k
R2   1k
R3   5k6
R4   1M8
R5   330R
R6   1M2
R7   1M2
R8   3k3
R9   330R
R10   10k
R11   56k
R12   33k
R13   3k9

R14	2M2
R15	1k
R16	100k
R17	2k2
R18	470k
R19	10k
R20	10k
R21	4k7
R22	1k5

Capacitors

C1	100μ 16V radial elect
C2	100μ 16V axial elect
C3	1n polyester or mylar
C4	4n7 polyester or mylar
C5	47n polyester or mylar
C6	3n3 polyester or mylar
C7	330n polyester or mylar
C8	1μ polyester
C9	10μ 25V radial elect
C10	220n polyester or mylar

Semiconductors

IC1	CA3130E
IC2	4013BE
IC3	4001BE
TR1	BP103B or similar (see text)
TR2	BC550
TR3	BC550
TR4	BC549
TR5	BC547
D1	1N4148
D2	1N4148
D3	1N4148
D4	1N4148
D5	Ultra bright 8 or 10mm l.e.d.

Miscellaneous

| S1, S2 | Normally closed sensor switches |
| S3, S4 | Normally open sensor switches |

S5	SPST key switch
L1	100mH low frequency inductor
B1	12 volt (8 × HP2/D size cells in plastic holder)
RLA/1	12 volt 270 ohm coil, SPDT 16A contacts (Maplin "12V 16A relay", Cat No. YX99H, or similar, see text)

Strong metal case, 0.1 inch pitch stripboard measuring 71 holes by 25 copper strips, 8-pin DIL holder, 14-pin d.i.l. holder (2 off), battery connector (PP3 type), wire, solder, etc.

Mains PSU

As pointed out previously, the supply voltage and current consumption of the remote controlled alarm circuit make battery power rather expensive in the long term. A mains power supply unit is a much more economic means of powering the alarm. The circuit requires a reasonably stable and well smoothed 12 volt supply. Figure 1.22 shows the circuit diagram for a suitable mains power supply unit (PSU). Incidentally, this power supply is also suitable for use with the basic switch activated alarm circuit.

This circuit is a conventional type having S1 to provide on/off switching, and mains transformer T1 to provide the necessary voltage step-down and isolation. D1 to D4 form a full-wave bridge rectifier, and C1 is the smoothing capacitor. FS1 provides protection against medium term overloads, but the main protection is provided by the built-in current limiting of IC1. This keeps the output current at a safe level in the event of a short circuit or other severe overload on the output. IC1 is a 12 volt 100 milliamp monolithic voltage regulator, and it provides a very well smoothed and regulated output to the alarm circuit. C2 and C3 are decoupling components which ensure IC1 does not become unstable. They must be fitted close to IC1, where they can have maximum effect.

PSU Construction

It is assumed here that the mains power supply unit will be built into the same case as the alarm circuit. It could be built as a

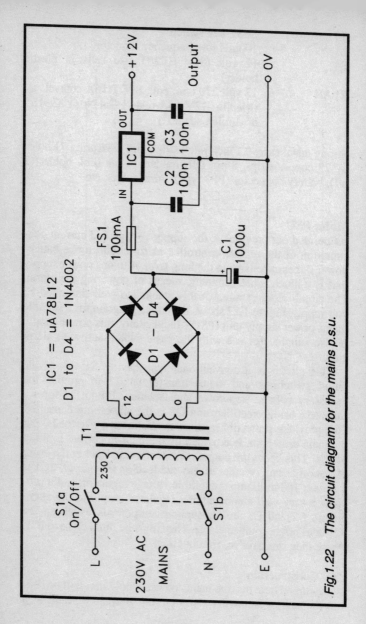

IC1 = uA78L12
D1 to D4 = 1N4002

Fig.1.22 The circuit diagram for the mains p.s.u.

42

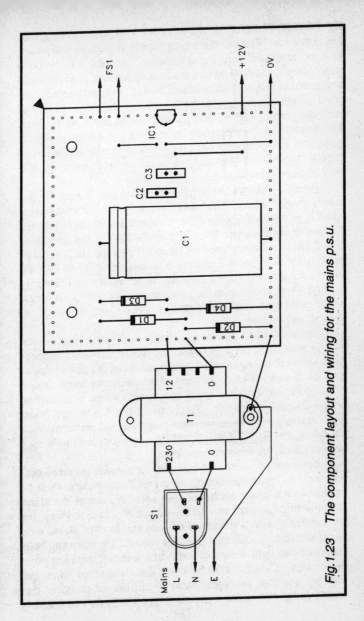

Fig.1.23   The component layout and wiring for the mains p.s.u.

43

separate unit if preferred, but there is no obvious advantage in this approach. Whether the power supply is built as a separate unit, or integrated with the controller, it should only be constructed by those who have a reasonable amount of experience at electronic project construction. Mains powered projects are not a suitable starting point for beginners. The mains supply is very dangerous, and mistakes could easily prove to be fatal. Those who lack the necessary experience and expertise should power the alarm circuit from a batteries, or a ready-made power supply capable of providing a stabilised 12 volts at 100 milliamps or more.

Figure 1.23 shows the stripboard layout and wiring for the mains power supply. The underside view of the component panel is provided in Figure 1.24. Construction of the stripboard follows along the same lines as construction of the controller board, but extra care should be taken in this case. In particular, make quite sure that C1 and the four rectifiers (D1 to D4) are fitted the right way round. Mistakes here could result in costly damage, and could even be dangerous. For similar reasons, make quite sure that the breaks in the copper strips are all present and correct.

There are actually one or two breaks in the strips that are not strictly necessary, but they reduce the risk of unwanted connections between the input and output sections of the circuit due to accidental short circuits between adjacent copper strips. These occur quite easily when using stripboard, where it is easy to bridge strips by applying slightly too much solder to a joint. You certainly need to be on your guard against problems with excess solder, and if a stripboard based project fails to work I always check for this problem first.

For reasons of safety it is essential for a mains powered project such as this to be housed in a metal case which must be earthed to the mains earth lead. For security reasons the alarm is likely to be housed in a heavy-duty metal case anyway, but for a mains powered version of the unit any form of plastic case is not suitable. A soldertag fitted on one of T1's mounting bolts represents an easy means of providing a secure earthing point on the case. The case must be a type that has a screw fixing lid, and not one that has some form of clip-on lid or cover that would make it easy for someone to get access to, and possibly

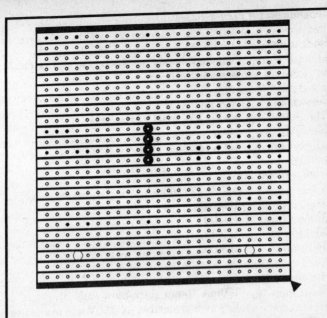

Fig.1.24   The underside of the mains p.s.u. board

touch, part of the dangerous mains wiring.

In Figure 1.23 S1 is shown as being a rotary mains switch, but it is of course in order to use other types, such as a toggle or a rocker switch. Make quite sure though, that the switch is rated to operate on the 230 volt a.c. mains supply. FS1 is mounted off-board in a panel mounting 20 millimetre fuse-holder. It is essential that the power supply board is mounted well clear of the case using spacers about 10 or 12 millimetres long. The hard wiring is very simple and straightforward, but take extra care here as some of the wiring connects direct to the mains supply. Double check the circuit board and all the wiring before testing the power supply.

45

Components for Figure 1.22

Transformer
T1   Standard mains primary, 12 volt 100mA secondary

Capacitors
C1   1000μ 25V axial electrolytic
C2   100n ceramic
C3   100n ceramic

Semiconductors
IC1   μA78L12 (100mA 12V positive regulator)
D1   1N4002
D2   1N4002
D3   1N4002
D4   1N4002

Miscellaneous
FS1   100mA 20mm quick-blow fuse
S1   Key switch suitable for 230V a.c. mains use

0.1 inch pitch stripboard having 24 holes by 24 copper strips, 20mm panel mounting fuse-holder, multi-strand connecting wire, mains plug (fitted with 2A or 3A fuse) and lead, single-sided solder pins, solder, etc.

Audio Alarm Generator
The two alarm circuits described previously will work with ready-made audio alarm generators, but low cost devices of this type are easily constructed. The audio alarm generator featured here produces a frequency modulated signal that gives a sort of warbling sound. Alarms are much more effective if the tone is modulated in some way. Apart from the fact that a changing sound tends to be more attention grabbing than a fixed tone, a modulated tone is less easily masked by other sounds. Frequency modulation is particularly effective, as it results in a wide range of frequencies being generated, which makes it difficult for other sounds to provide effective masking.

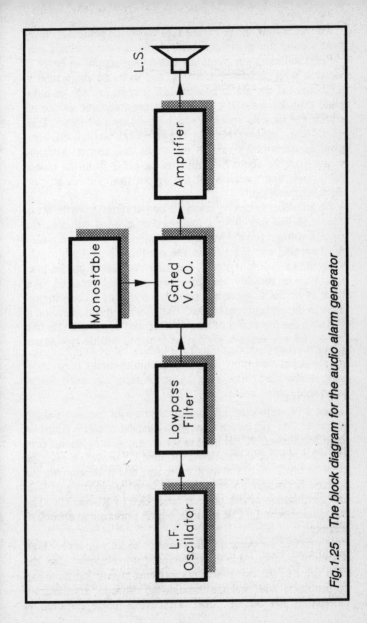

Fig. 1.25   The block diagram for the audio alarm generator

47

The block diagram of Figure 1.25 shows the general arrangement used in this alarm generator. A gated v.c.o. (voltage controlled oscillator) generates the basic tone signal. In order to conform with current regulations, and to avoid annoyance to neighbours if the alarm is activated, it must include an automatic shut-down facility. In this case the automatic switch-off is provided by a monostable which drives the gate input of the v.c.o. The monostable is triggered at switch-on, and provides a control signal to the v.c.o. that sets it operating normally. After about five minutes the pulse from the monostable ends and switches off the output from the v.c.o., thus silencing the alarm.

An amplifier is used to boost the output signal from the v.c.o. to a level that can drive a loudspeaker at good volume. The control voltage for the v.c.o. is provided by a low frequency oscillator and a lowpass filter. The oscillator provides a roughly squarewave output signal, but after processing by the lowpass filter a roughly triangular waveform is obtained. The linearity of the waveform is poor, but this is of no real importance in the present application. The effect of the modulation is to sweep the frequency of the v.c.o. up and down at a rate of a few cycles per second, giving the required warble-type alarm sound.

The Circuit

Figure 1.26 shows the full circuit diagram for the audio alarm generator. As will be apparent from this, the circuit is based on three 555 timers. IC1 is used in the monostable mode and provides the automatic shut-down. R1 and C2 provide a negative pulse to pin 2 of IC1 at switch-on, and this pulse triggers the device. A positive pulse is then produced at pin three of IC1, and the duration of this pulse is controlled by R2 and C3. The pulse duration is 1.1 C R seconds, which works out at about 290 seconds.

In practice the pulse duration can not be set with a very high degree of precision due to the component tolerances. Also, the high value of the two timing components means that there can be problems with leakage through the capacitor significantly elongating the output pulse. The actual pulse duration is

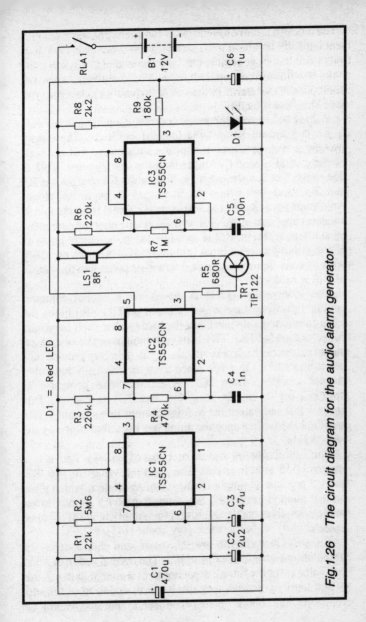

Fig.1.26   The circuit diagram for the audio alarm generator

49

therefore likely to be somewhat more than 290 seconds, and will typically be a little over 5 minutes (300 seconds). Note that unless C3 is a high quality capacitor the output pulse will continue indefinitely. A tantalum capacitor is relatively expensive but represents the safest option. A high quality electrolytic type should suffice though.

IC2 is used in the tone generator circuit, and this is basically just a standard 555 astable (oscillator) circuit. The output waveform from pin three is almost a squarewave, but the high output period is slightly longer than the low duration. This is due to the fact that the output is high while C4 charges via R3 and R4, and low while it discharges through R4 alone. Anything approximating to a squarewave signal is acceptable in an alarm application. R3, R4, and C4 set the operating frequency at about 1.24kHz. IC2 is gated by using the output pulse of IC1 to control its reset input (pin four). IC2 operates normally with its reset input taken high, but with it taken low the output of IC2 is held low.

The loudspeaker (LS1) is driven via a simple common emitter switching stage which is based on TR1. R5 limits the drive current to a safe level, and the loudspeaker itself forms the collector load for TR1. TR1 is a Darlington power device which has an extremely high current gain. It can therefore provide output currents of up to a few amps from the relatively low drive current available from IC2. When the tone generator is switched off its output goes low, and TR1 is cut off. This ensures that only a minute leakage current flows through TR1 and the loudspeaker once the alarm has been shut-down by the monostable.

The low frequency oscillator is based on IC3, and it is a standard 555 astable circuit. The specified values for R6, R7, and C5 produce an output frequency of about 6Hz, which gives quite a good alarm sound. Some might prefer a slightly lower modulation frequency though, and this simply requires R7 to be made slightly higher in value (say about 1M5).

R9 and C6 form the lowpass filter, and this couples the modulation signal to pin five of IC2. The normal action of a 555 oscillator is for the timing capacitor to first charge to two-thirds of the supply potential, then discharge to one third of the supply potential, charge up to two thirds of the supply voltage again, and so on. Pin five connects to an internal potential divider which sets the two thirds of the supply voltage threshold level. Pulling this voltage higher results in C4 taking longer to charge to the threshold voltage, and longer to discharge from it. The output frequency is therefore reduced. Pulling the threshold voltage lower means that C4 charges to and discharges from the threshold level in less time, giving a higher output frequency. Varying the voltage on IC2 pin five therefore gives the required frequency modulation, with the output frequency being varied around its normal figure of 1.24kHz.

D1 is simply a l.e.d. indicator which is switched on while power is applied to the alarm generator. It will remain switched on once the alarm has shut itself down, indicating to the user that the alarm has been activated. The circuit is switched on via a set of normally open relay contacts (RLA1) in the main alarm circuit.

The circuit is powered from a 12 volt battery which must be a fairly high capacity type since the current consumption of the circuit is in the region of 750 milliamps with the alarm sounding. Quite high volume levels are obtained using an eight ohm impedance loudspeaker, but if required the output power can be doubled by using a four ohm impedance loudspeaker. This doubles the current consumption to about 1.5 amps. The current consumption of the circuit is only about five milliamps after the alarm has automatically shut down. This ensures that the batteries are not seriously run down if the unit is left switched on for some time after it has been activated.

Of course, until the alarm is activated the audio alarm generator is completely disconnected from the battery supply, and has zero current consumption. Each set of batteries should therefore have its "shelf life", which these days is normally a couple of years or more. The circuit can be powered from a mains power supply unit if preferred, and this should be capable of supplying a reasonably well smoothed and regulated 12 volt supply at either 750 milliamps or 1.5 amps, depending on the impedance of the loudspeaker used.

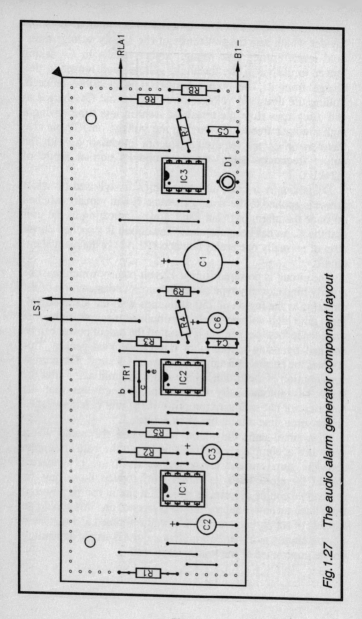

Fig. 1.27   The audio alarm generator component layout

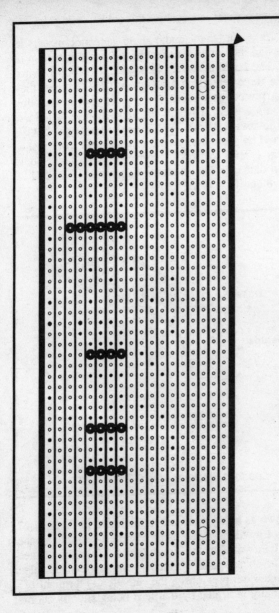

Fig.1.28   The underside view of the audio alarm generator board

53

Construction

The stripboard layout for the audio alarm generator appears in Figure 1.27, and the underside view of the board is shown in Figure 1.28. The board measures 49 holes by 18 copper strips. Although the three integrated circuits are CMOS types, they have built-in protection circuits that render special handling precautions unnecessary. I would still urge the use of holders for all three devices. TR1 is a TIP121 on the prototype, but the TIP122 offered by some component retailers will work just as well. Be very careful to fit TR1 correctly as mistakes could cause costly damage. The leadout diagram of Figure 1.29 should help to clarify matters.

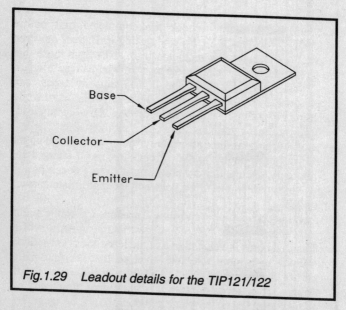

Fig.1.29   Leadout details for the TIP121/122

D1 is shown as being mounted on the board in Figure 1.27, but in practice it will normally be mounted off-board in a panel holder, and hard wired to the circuit board. Make the connections to the stripboard panel via a couple of single-sided solder pins. As pointed out previously, the cathode (+) terminal of a l.e.d. is normally indicated by that lead being slightly shorter, and by a "flat" on that side of the body. In Figure 1.27 the polarity of D1 is indicated by the "flat" on its body.

Transistor TR1 does not have to dissipate much power due to its switching mode of operation. Also, it will only operate for about five minutes at a time due to the automatic shut-down circuit. It is still advisable to ensure cool and safe operation by fitting it with a small clip-on or bolt-on heatsink, especially if a four ohm impedance loudspeaker is used. Alternatively, a home constructed heatsink consisting of a few square centimetres of 18 or 16 s.w.g. aluminium should be more than adequate. Bear in mind that the collector of TR1 connects internally to its heat-tab. Make sure that no exposed wires come into contact with TR1's heat-tab or with the heatsink.

As this project involves quite high operating currents it is essential to thoroughly check the completed unit before connecting it to the 12 supply and testing it. Battery powered projects do not normally include a fuse, apart from those that are powered from something like a car or boat battery. Modern "dry" batteries, particularly the higher capacity types, can supply quite high currents though, and it might be worthwhile including a two amp fuse in series with the positive supply lead, particularly during initial testing. An "anti-surge" or "delay" fuse should be used, since an ordinary "quick-blow" type might "blow" at switch-on due to the current surge as C1 charges up. Alternatively, test the unit by powering it from a bench power supply set for an output of 12 volts and an appropriate current limit setting.

If working properly the unit should produce a piercing alarm sound at high volume. I would suggest adding a resistor of a few hundred ohms in value in one of the leads to LS1 to reduce the volume to a more tolerable level so that the automatic switch-off facility can be checked. If the alarm fails to cut off after about six or seven minutes it is likely that the quality of C3 is inadequate. The problem could probably be cured by making R2 lower in value, but it is better to replace C3 with a higher quality component.

Components for Figure 1.26

Resistors (all 0.25 watt 5% carbon film)
R1	22k
R2	5M6
R3	220k
R4	470k
R5	680R
R6	220k
R7	1M
R8	2k2
R9	180k

Capacitors
C1	470µ 16V radial elect
C2	2µ2 63V radial elect
C3	47µ high quality radial elect or tantalum
C4	1n polyester
C5	100n polyester

Semiconductors
IC1	TS555CN
IC2	TS555CN
IC3	TS555CN
TR1	TIP121 or TIP122
D1	5mm Red l.e.d.

Miscellaneous
LS1	8 ohm loudspeaker rated at 10 watts r.m.s. or more, or 4 ohm loudspeaker rated at 20 watts r.m.s. or more
RLA1	Part of main alarm circuit
B1	12 volts (e.g. eight HP2 size cells in plastic holders)

Case, stripboard measuring 49 holes by 18 copper strips, small TO220 bolt-on or clip-on heatsink, 8-pin DIL holder (3 off), panel holder for D1, wire, solder, etc.

Mains Power Supply

The mains power supply unit described previously is not suitable for use with the audio alarm generator, due to the alarm generator's relatively high current consumption. However, with a certain amount of modification the output current of the supply can be boosted to a suitable level. The circuit diagram for the modified mains power supply circuit is provided in Figure 1.30.

This is much the same as the original, but mains transformer T1 has higher voltage ratings of 15 volts and must have a current rating of 1.2 amps or more. The value of C1 has been increased from 1000µ to 2200µ in order to maintain adequate smoothing. IC1 is a one amp regulator, rather than the 100 milliamp type of the original circuit.

The supply can be constructed using the same general layout, etc., as the original (Figures 1.31 and 1.32), but there are a few points to note. IC1 has to dissipate several watts while the alarm is sounding, and it requires a certain amount of heatsinking in order to ensure that it does not overheat. One of the larger bolt-on heatsinks having a rating of about 10 degrees Celsius per watt is the minimum requirement. Some monolithic voltage regulators have an isolated heat-tab, but with most types there is an internal connection from the ground lead-out wire to the heat-tab. Be careful to fit IC1 correctly. The leadout diagram of Figure 1.33 should help in this respect.

Mains transformer T1 will probably have to be a type which has twin 15 volt secondary windings rated at about 800 milliamps or so. These are wired in parallel (as shown in Figure 1.31) to produce what is effectively a single 15 volt winding having a current rating of about 1.6 amps. This method should only be used with a twin secondary transformer that is designed for series or parallel connection. These days most mains transformers seem to be of this type, but if the retailer's literature does not specifically say that a transformer can operate with its secondaries connected in parallel, it must be assumed that it can not. As with the original power supply design, it must be constructed to comply with the normal safety regulations, and should not be constructed by beginners unless they are properly supervised by someone who has the requisite experience of electronic project construction.

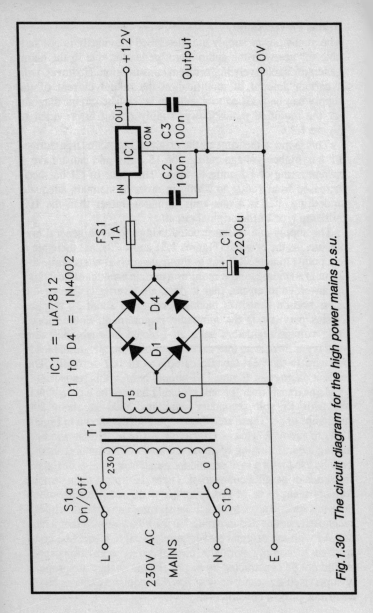

Fig.1.30   The circuit diagram for the high power mains p.s.u.

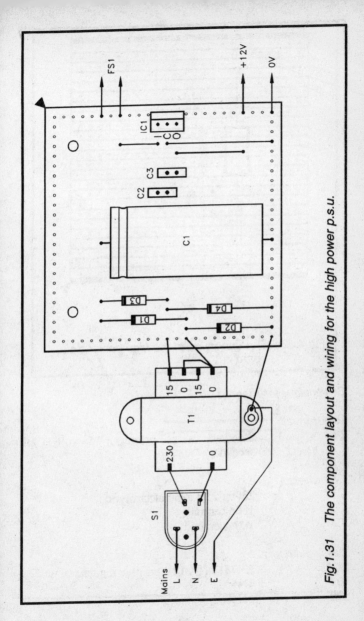

Fig.1.31   The component layout and wiring for the high power p.s.u.

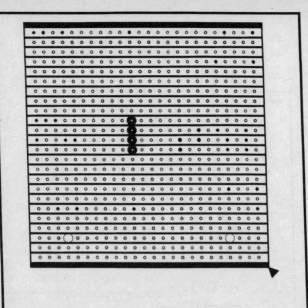

*Fig.1.32   The underside of the high power p.s.u.
board*

Components for Figure 1.30

Transformer
T1   Standard mains primary, 15 volt 1.2A
                secondary (see text)

Capacitors
C1   2200µ 25V axial electrolytic
C2   100n ceramic
C3   100n ceramic

Semiconductors
IC1   µA7812 (1A 12V positive regulator)
D1   1N4002
D2   1N4002

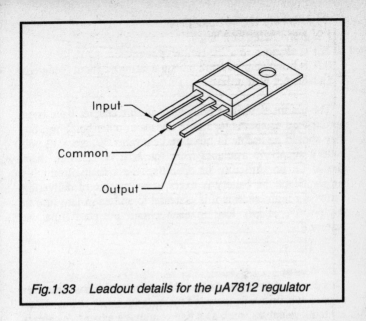

Fig.1.33 Leadout details for the µA7812 regulator

| D3 | 1N4002 |
| D4 | 1N4002 |

Miscellaneous

| FS1 | 1A 20mm quick-blow fuse |
| S1 | Key switch suitable for 230V a.c. mains use |

0.1 inch pitch stripboard having 24 holes by 24 copper strips, 20mm panel mounting fuse-holder, multi-strand connecting wire, mains plug (fitted with 2A or 3A fuse) and lead, single-sided solder pins, solder, etc.

In theory, the mains power supply can be used with an alarm generator that drives a four ohm impedance loudspeaker provided the following modifications are made. Note though, that I have not tried this in practice.

The current rating of T1 is increased to at least 2.4 amps
The value of C1 is raised to 4700µ

D1 to D4 are 1N5402 rectifiers
FS1 has a rating of 2 amps
IC1 is changed to a 78S12 2 amp regulator
IC1 is fitted on a heatsink having a rating of about 5 degrees
Celsius per watt or less

The alarms described previously in this chapter have been put forward as alarms for use in houses or other buildings, but they should be usable in boats and caravans. Where a 12 volt battery supply is available from the boat or caravan, there should be no difficulty in operating the circuits from this supply. Since the battery is likely to be capable of delivering extremely high currents it is essential to add an in-line fuse in the positive supply lead to each circuit powered from the battery.

Case Alarm

This design is for a simple portable alarm which has a number of uses. It is primarily intended for use with a case or bag which contains valuables, such as a bag containing expensive camera equipment. The idea is to switch on the alarm whenever the bag is put down for a while. The alarm is triggered by movement, and it will be activated if anyone tries to make off with the bag. It will probably be triggered if someone tampers with the bag, with a view to stealing something from it, but this obviously depends on how easily something can be removed from the bag. It is always a bad idea to leave a bag open so that valuables can be quickly and easily removed. No alarm is likely to be of any use in a situation of that kind.

Although primarily intended for use with cases and bags, an alarm of this type can be used to protect other items of equipment. In particular, they are often fitted to expensive items of electronic equipment, such as video recorders and computers. Anyone trying to make off with the protected device will get a shock when they move it and the alarm goes off. They might decide to make off with the unit, complete with the activated alarm, but most thieves will simply lose their nerve and make their escape empty handed.

Trembler Switch

The block diagram of Figure 1.34 shows the general make-up of the case alarm. It is based on a trembler switch, which is normally a form of mercury switch. These components are also known as vibration switches incidentally. A normal mercury switch is basically just a container made from an insulating material, and fitted with an electrode at each end. The container is partially filled with mercury. At certain orientations the mercury bridges the two electrodes and provides an electrical contact between them, while at other orientations it does not.

An ordinary mercury switch is usable in an alarm of the type featured here, but is less than perfect. Ideally the sensor switch should provide no contact between the electrodes when it is stationary, but should bridge the contacts if it is disturbed. Most trembler switches utilize a slight variation on the basic mercury switch scheme of things. They vary somewhat from one type to another, but mostly they have two intricately shaped electrodes at the centre of a slightly less than half filled reservoir of mercury. With the switch held still the mercury will fail to touch both electrodes, regardless of the switch's orientation. Since the mercury only just fails to bridge the electrodes when the switch is stationary, it only takes slight movement to send waves through the mercury that result in the switch closing momentarily.

This alarm will work properly using an ordinary mercury switch, but a trembler switch is much more convenient in use. With an ordinary mercury switch it essential to mount the switch with an orientation that results in it being switched off, but only just. Then, with luck, any slight movement of the case will cause the switch to close at least momentarily. A trembler switch can be mounted with any orientation, and will give the desired effect. You can therefore simply throw the alarm anywhere into the case and it will work properly, with no need to fix it in place in a particular position. These days some "tilt" switches are not actually mercury switches, but any form of "tilt" or "vibration" switch should be suitable for use in this project provided it is reasonably small.

Returning to the block diagram of Figure 1.34, the trembler switch will only make momentary contact when it is activated. The switch therefore drives a bistable which latches its output

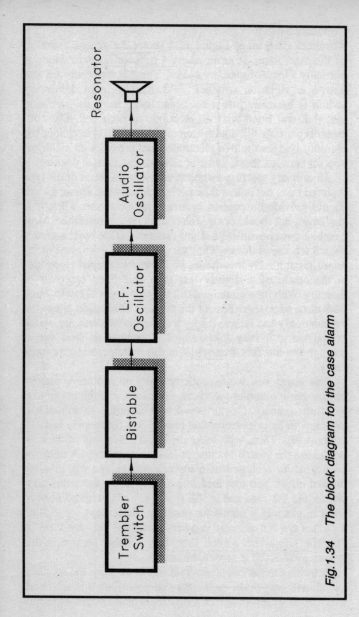

Fig. 1.34   The block diagram for the case alarm

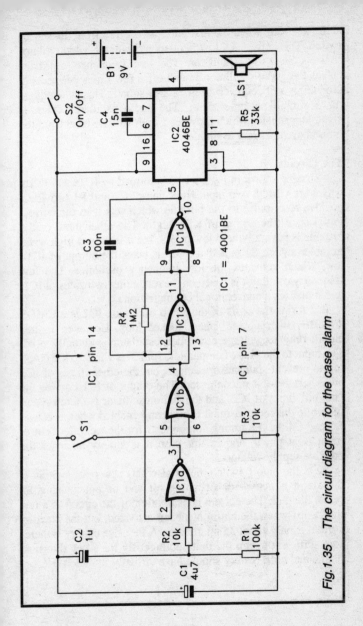

Fig. 1.35   The circuit diagram for the case alarm

in the low state when the first pulse is received from the sensor switch. This activates a low frequency oscillator, which in turn controls an audio oscillator. The low frequency oscillator pulses the audio oscillator on and off a few times per second, producing a "beep-beep-beep" alarm sound. This is adequate for a simple portable alarm. The audio oscillator drives a ceramic resonator which provides a high volume level from the limited drive current available.

The Circuit

The bistable shown in Figure 1.35 is formed by IC1a and IC1b, which are CMOS two input NOR gates. C2 and R1 provide a positive reset pulse to the bistable which sets it to the correct initial state (the output of IC1b high). The other input of the bistable is normally held low by R3, but it is pulsed high when trembler switch S1 is activated. This takes the output of IC1b low, which activates the low frequency oscillator. The low frequency oscillator is based on the remaining two gates of IC1, and it utilizes a conventional configuration.

IC2 forms the basis of the audio oscillator. IC2 is a CMOS 4046BE "micropower" phase locked loop. However, in this circuit only its voltage controlled oscillator is actually used. The input to the phase comparators (pin 3) is wired to the 0 volt rail to prevent spurious operations, but the other stages of IC2 are otherwise left unconnected. The output of IC1d drives the "inhibit" input of IC2, and the audio oscillator is therefore cut off while the control signal is high, and enabled when it is low. R5 and C4 are the timing components for the v.c.o. Its control input is at pin 9, and in this case it is simply taken to the positive supply voltage.

S2 is the on/off switch, but it also acts as a reset switch. If the alarm is activated, switching off and on again using S2 resets the unit. The current consumption of the circuit is a few milliamps when the alarm has been activated, but the standby current is only about 35 microamps. A PP3 size battery is therefore sufficient to run the unit continuously for a few thousand hours, and each battery should have virtually its "shelf life."

Construction

Details of the stripboard layout for the case alarm are provided in Figure 1.36 (component side) and Figure 1.37 (copper side). Construction of the board is largely straightforward, but remember that both integrated circuits are CMOS types, and that the normal anti-static handling precautions are required when dealing with them.

LS1 must be a cased ceramic resonator and not an ordinary moving-coil loudspeaker. The available drive current is too low to give a worthwhile volume level from an ordinary loud-speaker. Also, a loudspeaker could overload IC2 and damage its output stage. Ceramic resonators often seem to have one red lead and one black lead. They are not polarised components though, and LS1 can be connected either way round. The colour coding of the leads presumably indicates the phasing of the component, which is irrelevant in this application. The volume level should be quite high, but it might be possible to obtain even higher volume by "tweaking" the value of R5 to find the frequency at which the resonator offers peak efficiency.

The trembler switch might be in the form of a (mainly) metal casing with two tags. If so, it should be glued to the case with a good quality general purpose adhesive such as an epoxy type. Two insulated leads are then used to connect it to the board via a couple solder pins fitted to the board at the appropriate two positions. These days the trembler switch is more likely to be in the form of a small metal encapsulation having a single mounting pin. With this type of switch the single pin is soldered to the board. The second connection is then made to the metal encapsulation, and there seems to be no difficulty in making a good connection when soldering an insulated lead to the case. The other end of the lead connects to the board via the usual solder pin.

S2 could be a key-switch, but the expense of even a fairly basic key-switch is probably not justified in this case. Once the alarm has been set off it should almost immediately warn the user that the bag or case is being tampered with. The would-be thief could probably locate the alarm quite quickly once it had been set off, and then switch it off, but it would be too late. The main danger of using a simple on/off switch is that the would-be thief might manage to locate and deactivate the alarm

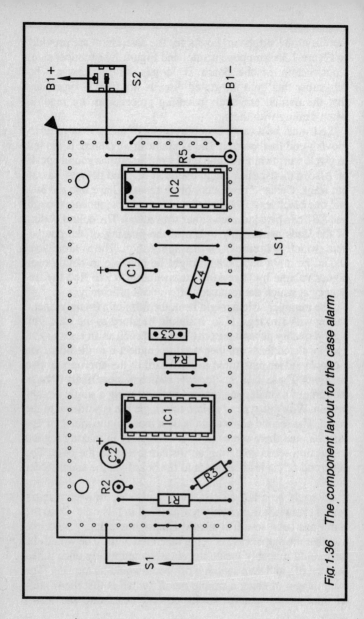

Fig. 1.36   The component layout for the case alarm

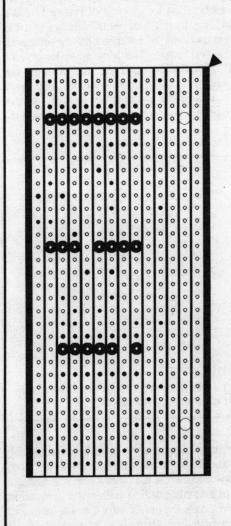

Fig. 1.37   The underside of the case alarm board

before triggering it. It obviously helps in this respect if the user does his or her best to conceal the presence of the alarm.

If something more than a simple on/off switch is preferred, the simple combination lock circuit of Figure 1.38 is a good choice. This is basically just four on/off switches wired in parallel, so the alarm can only be switched off by setting all four switches to the "off" state. The trick is to have some switches set to "off" when the lever is in the "up" position, and others set to "off" when it is in the down position. Also, leave the unit with one or two of the switches set to "off", so that simply reversing the position of each switch will not turn off the alarm.

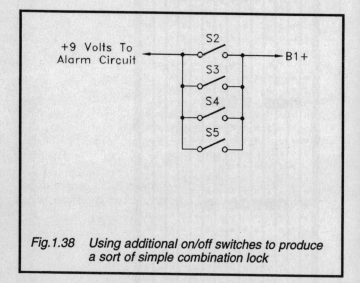

Fig.1.38   Using additional on/off switches to produce a sort of simple combination lock

The vibration switches I have used have been reasonably sensitive, but there should be no great problem with the alarm triggering as it is switched on. On the other hand, it is essential to have the alarm in a stable position within the case before turning it on, and to operate the on/off switch or switches with reasonable care if unwanted triggering is to be avoided.

Components for Figure 1.35

Resistors (all 0.25 watt 5% carbon film)
R1   100k
R2   10k
R3   10k
R4   1M2
R5   33k

Capacitors
C1   4µ7 63V radial elect
C2   1µ 63V radial elect
C3   100n polyester
C4   15n polyester

Semiconductors
IC1   4001BE
IC2   4046BE

Miscellaneous
S1   Trembler switch
S2   SPST min toggle switch
LS1   Cased ceramic resonator
B1   9 volt (PP3 size)

Small case, stripboard measuring 31 holes by 14 copper strips, 14-pin DIL holder, 16-pin DIL holder, battery connector, wire, solder, etc.

Chapter 2

EXOTICA

Standard switch sensor alarms were covered in Chapter 1, and in this chapter we progress to more exotic alarms and sensors which utilize such things as fibre-optics, ultrasonics, and infra-red "light". We start with two loop alarms which make use of the fibre-optic cables that are now readily available from some of the larger electronic component retailers. An alarm of this type is used for protecting goods that are on display in a shop (or on a market stall), and conventionally the loop is a loop of wire.

The alarm works along the general lines shown in Figure 2.1, where the loop of wire is threaded through the handles of the items to be protected. The latter could be some transistor radios, handbags, bracelets, or anything that can be threaded onto the piece of wire. The wire is connected into a simple

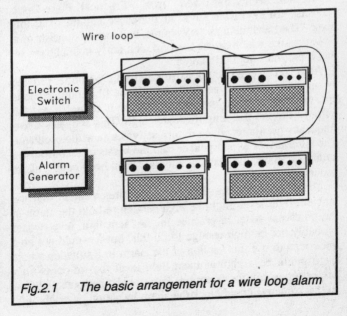

Fig.2.1   *The basic arrangement for a wire loop alarm*

circuit that operates an audible alarm if someone cuts the wire in attempt to steal some of the protected items.

An alarm of this type is quite effective, but a determined thief could defeat the alarm by bypassing part of the loop before cutting the wire and making of with the spoils. A loop alarm which uses a fibre-optic cable rather than a simple piece of wire is slightly more expensive, but is virtually "uncrackable". Electrically bypassing a piece of wire, even while it is carrying a signal, is quite easy, but bypassing a fibre-optic cable is extremely difficult. While it is probably technically feasible, bypassing a fibre-optic cable is very difficult in practice. Trying it would almost certainly trigger the alarm, and anyone undertaking intricate tampering with the cable would soon be spotted anyway.

D.C. Alarm

In its most simple form a fibre-optic alarm uses a non-modulated signal through the cable. Figure 2.2 shows the block diagram for a simple d.c. coupled loop alarm of this type. This circuit has been "borrowed" from "Practical Fibre-Optic Projects" (BP374) from the same publisher and author as this book. The transmitter is very simple, and merely consists of a power source which drives the l.e.d. at a fairly high current so that it provides high brightness.

At the receiver a phototransistor and a d.c. amplifier provide an output level that is normally low. If the fibre-optic cable is cut, the light level to the phototransistor is reduced, and the output from the d.c. amplifier goes high. This activates a low frequency oscillator, which in turn activates an audio oscillator. The latter drives a loudspeaker, and the bursts of tone from the audio oscillator produce a simple "beep-beep-beep" alarm sound.

There is an obvious flaw in this arrangement in that the ambient light level might be high enough to hold the alarm in the quiescent state. In practice the ambient light level would probably not be high enough to do this, but it would not be a good idea to use this version of the alarm in a situation where there might be a high ambient light level (out-of-doors on a bright sunny day for example). There is another potential flaw in that someone could block the alarm by shining a bright light

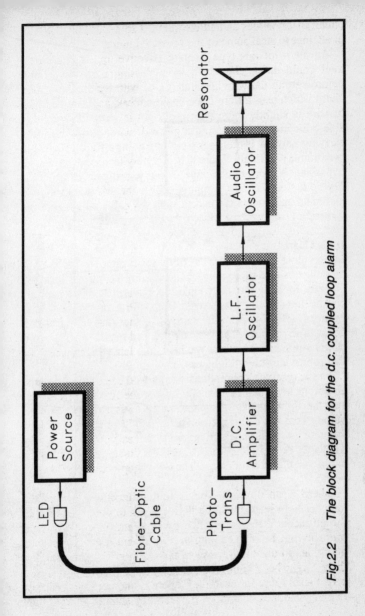

Fig.2.2   The block diagram for the d.c. coupled loop alarm

75

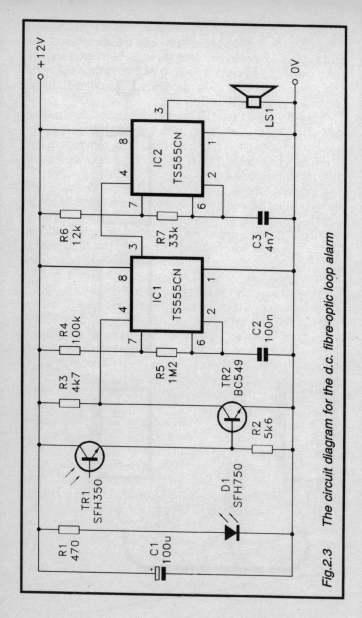

Fig.2.3   The circuit diagram for the d.c. fibre-optic loop alarm

76

into the appropriate cut end of the cable. This is not very likely though, as they would need to know how the alarm works, and which piece of cable to feed from the light source. Anyway, the alarm would almost certainly sound for a short time before the light source could be put into place, which should be sufficient to alert the shop or stall holder.

Figure 2.3 shows the full circuit diagram for the d.c. loop alarm. D1 is the l.e.d. and R1 is its current limiting resistor. The l.e.d. current is about 20 milliamps. This is high enough to give good l.e.d. brightness, but is within the maximum current rating of any normal l.e.d.

The receiver has TR1 and TR2 in a simple direct coupled arrangement. TR2 operates as a common emitter switch, and with phototransistor TR1 receiving a low light level TR2 is switched off. This is due to the fact that under dark conditions TR1 has the very low leakage level associated with normal silicon transistors. The leakage level increases massively when TR1 is subjected to bright conditions, which results in TR2 being biased into conduction. Therefore, the collector of TR1 is low while the loop is present and correct, but it goes high if the loop is broken and the light from D1 no longer reaches TR1.

The specified value for R2 gives reasonable sensitivity, and the circuit should work using a cable of up to about 8 metres in length. For optimum results R2 should be replaced with a 10k preset resistor. This should be adjusted for the highest sensitivity (highest value) that holds the alarm in the "off" state under standby conditions.

The alarm generator is based on two 555 gated astable circuits. IC1 is used in the low frequency oscillator, and its operating frequency is a little under 3Hz. The gate signal is applied to pin 4, which is actually the reset input. However, it functions well as a gate input, and switches off the oscillator if it is held below approximately 0.5 volts. IC2 is used in exactly the same configuration, but its timing component values set the operating frequency at a little under 2kHz. LS1 is a cased ceramic resonator, and a component of this type provides good efficiency at this fairly high audio frequency. Note that LS1 should only be a ceramic resonator, and not an ordinary moving coil loudspeaker. Trying to use a moving coil loudspeaker with this circuit could result in IC2 being damaged, and will not provide a worthwhile alarm sound.

The typical current consumption of the circuit is slightly in excess of 20 milliamps. The circuit could be powered from a high capacity 12 volt battery, but a mains power supply unit is a more practical choice unless portable operation is required. The low power design described in chapter 1 (Figure 1.22) is suitable for this project. Alternatively, a ready-made power supply unit which can provide a well smoothed and regulated supply at about 30 milliamps or more should suffice. The circuit might not work properly if powered from an inexpensive "battery eliminator" that has an unregulated 12 volt output containing a high noise and ripple level.

Construction

The component layout for the stripboard panel appears in Figure 2.4, and the underside view of the board is shown in Figure 2.5. The board measures 43 holes by 18 copper strips.

The specified l.e.d. (D1) and phototransistor (TR1) are specifically designed for use with fibre-optic cables. The SFH750 is basically just a standard l.e.d. having a sort of hollowed-out encapsulation that enables the fibre-optic cable to be inserted into the front of the component. The cathode (+) lead is indicated by the usual "flat" on the body of the component, and the cathode lead being somewhat shorter than the anode lead. The SFH350 phototransistor has a similar encapsulation, but with three leadout wires. The "flat" on the casing and the shorter lead indicate the emitter leadout wire. Be very careful to get TR1 connected the right way round, as a mistake here could easily result in both TR1 and TR2 being destroyed. Figure 2.6 shows leadout diagrams for both the SFH350 and the SFH750.

The circuit should work properly using other l.e.d.s and phototransistors intended for use with fibre-optic cables. However, other phototransistors might require some adjustment of R2's value in order to obtain good results. Alternatively, replace R2 with a 22k preset resistor which can then be adjusted for optimum results in the manner described previously. It is possible to modify a standard five millimetre diameter l.e.d. for use with a fibre-optic cable. It is basically just a matter of filing the front of the component flat, and then drilling it with a hole of about 2.3 millimetres in diameter to take the fibre-optic

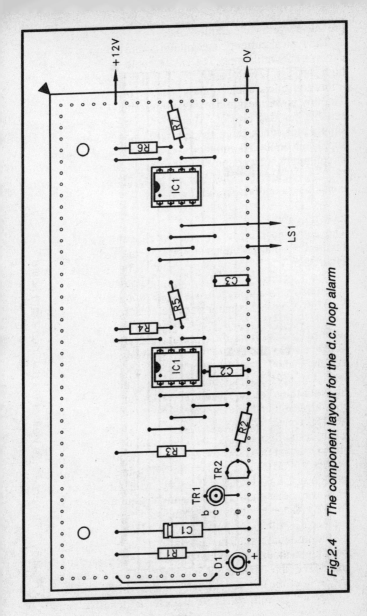

Fig.2.4 The component layout for the d.c. loop alarm

79

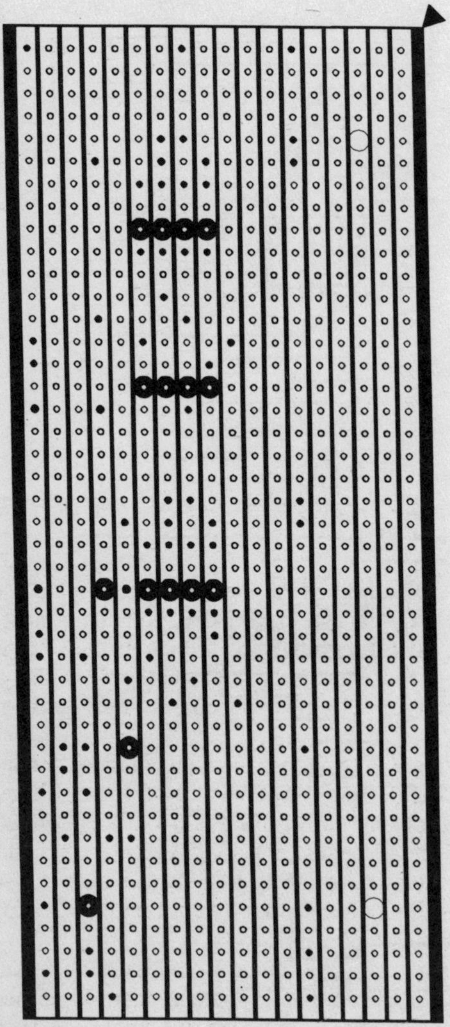

Fig.2.5 The underside view of the d.c. loop alarm board

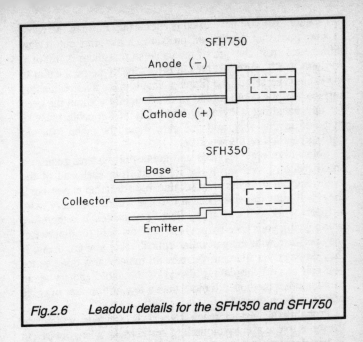

Fig.2.6   Leadout details for the SFH350 and SFH750

cable. In order to obtain good results it is necessary to use a "super bright" or "ultra-bright" l.e.d. Also, great care must be taken not to drill right trough the lens section of the l.e.d. and into the semiconductor chip. Using the "real thing" is likely to be much easier than improvising using conventional l.e.d.s and phototransistors.

Use standard single filament cable having an outer diameter of 2.2 millimetres and a filament diameter of one millimetre. Other types will probably not fit into the photocells correctly, and might not give satisfactory results anyway. As supplied, most fibre-optic cables have rather roughly cut ends. Cables with rough ends will not work properly until both ends of the cable have been properly prepared.

There are all-sorts of cable cutting devices and polishes available, but for simple fibre-optic systems there is no need to go to great lengths when preparing the cables. All you really need is a sharp modelling knife and a cutting board. The latter can simply be a thick piece of card or even just an old

81

newspaper. All you have to do is cut cleanly through the cable in one go using plenty of pressure. Make the cut a few millimetres from the end of the cable so that there is minimal wastage, and be sure that the cut is reasonably perpendicular to the cable. The end of the filament should have a smooth shiny surface, and the cable should work efficiently without the need for any polishing. Obviously both ends of the cable must be prepared in this way, and due care should be taken to avoid cutting yourself or the worktop.

Some fibre-optic devices and connector systems require a small piece of sleeving to be removed from each end of the cable. Special strippers are available, but are rather expensive if they will only receive occasional use. Some ordinary wire strippers work well with many fibre-optic cables. It is therefore worth trying your wire strippers to see how well (or otherwise) they perform with the particular optical cable you are using. If they damage the filament there is no major harm done, since you can cut off the damaged end of the cable and try again using another method. No more than a few millimetres of cable will have been wasted.

Probably the best approach if your wire strippers will not do the job is to use a sharp modelling knife. Make a lengthwise cut in the sleeving at the end of the cable. Try to cut reasonably deeply, but if possible avoid cutting into the polymer filament. It should then be possible to peel back the sleeving over the full length of the cut. The peeled-back section of sleeving is easily cut away using the modelling knife or a small but sharp pair of scissors. If might take one or two attempts to get it just right, but even if there should be a slight score mark in the exposed filament, it is unlikely that this will greatly reduce the efficiency of the cable. On the other hand, a deep cut into the filament will almost certainly prevent the cable from giving satisfactory results.

The SFH350 and SFH750 have no built-in method of clamping the cable in place, and it will pull out of either device with a minimum of effort. In order to avoid frequent false alarms it is essential to use something like small cable grips to secure both ends of the cable to the case of the alarm. This should not be difficult, but be careful not to clamp down the cables so tightly that the polymer filament becomes damaged.

Apart from dealing with the fibre-optics, construction of the unit is largely straightforward. The cased ceramic resonator will probably have red and black flying leads, but it can in fact be connected with either polarity. IC1 and IC2 can be any low power versions of the 555 timer. The circuit should also work if standard 555s are used, but the current consumption will be about 15 milliamps higher. Low power versions of the 555 are mostly based on CMOS technology, but they have static protection circuits that render any special handling precautions unnecessary.

Testing the completed unit is very simple. With the cable fitted to the photocells the alarm should not sound. Disconnecting the cable from one of the photocells should result in the "beep-beep-beep" alarm sound being produced immediately. If the alarm sounds even when the cable is in position, try the system with a very short piece of cable. If it works correctly with a short cable, then the problem is that the longer cable is not providing enough light to the photocell. Raising the value of R2 would probably correct this, but it would also increase the risk of the ambient light level holding the alarm in the "off" state. It would be better to settle for a slightly shorter cable.

Components for Figure 2.3

Resistors (all 0.25 watt 5% carbon film)

R1	470R
R2	5k6
R3	4k7
R4	100k
R5	1M2
R6	12k
R7	33k

Capacitors

C1	100µ 16V elect
C2	100n polyester
C3	4n7 polyester

Semiconductors

IC1	TS555CN or similar
IC2	TS555CN or similar
TR1	SFH350
TR2	BC549
D1	SFH750

Miscellaneous

LS1	Cased ceramic resonator

Case, stripboard measuring 43 holes by 18 copper strips, fibre-optic cable, 8 pin DIL IC holder (2 off), wire, solder, etc.

1/2.2 fibre-optic cable is available from:

Maplin Electronics Ltd.,
P.O. Box 3,
Rayleigh,
Essex,
SS6 2BR.
(Tel. 01702 554000)

The SFH350 and SFH750 are available from:

Electrovalue Ltd.,
Unit 3,
Central Trading Estate,
Staines,
TW18 4UX.
(Tel. 01784 442253)

Modulated Loop Alarm
Greater reliability can be obtained from a fibre-optic loop alarm by using some form of modulated light source. This also enables a larger loop to used. The advantage of using a modulated light source is that it provides a signal that is easily distinguished from the background light level which generally changes at a relatively slow rate. It also enables a.c. coupling to be used in the receiver circuit, which enables high sensitivity to

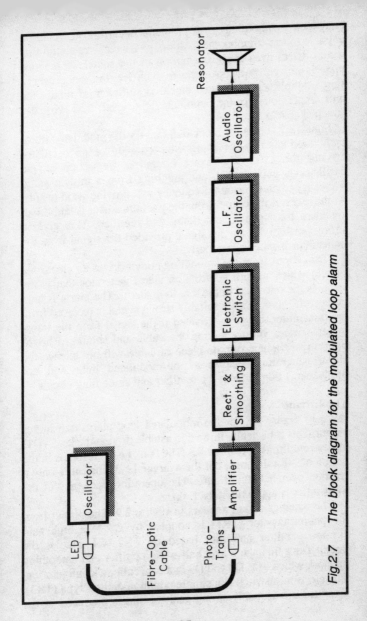

Fig.2.7 The block diagram for the modulated loop alarm

be obtained without any drift problems occurring. It would be possible to use complex modulation, plus a receiver circuit that would detect even slight corruption of the signal. In practice there is no real point in going to such lengths, since even a simple amplitude modulated signal is sufficient to render the unit impervious to the ambient light level, and virtually "uncrackable".

Figure 2.7 shows the block diagram for the modulated fibre-optic loop alarm. The transmitter consists of an oscillator driving the l.e.d. The exact operating frequency of the oscillator is unimportant, and anything from a middle audio frequency to an ultrasonic frequency will provide good results. At the receiver the output from the phototransistor is amplified, and then the signal is smoothed and rectified. This gives a strong positive d.c. output signal provided the signal from the transmitter is received properly.

The output from the smoothing circuit drives an electronic switch, which in turn controls an alarm generator that is the same as the one used in the d.c. loop alarm. The alarm is held in the "off" state when a suitably strong signal is received from the transmitter, but it is activated if the signal from the trans-mitter ceases. Simply cutting the cable and shining a bright light down the appropriate piece of cable will not silence the alarm generator, because a non-modulated light will not produce any output from the rectifier and smoothing circuit.

The Circuit

Refer to Figure 2.8 for the modulated loop alarm transmitter circuit. This is basically just a 555 astable driving the l.e.d. (D1) via current limiting resistor R3. The "on" l.e.d. current is in the region of 30 milliamps, but the average l.e.d. current is only a fraction over half this figure. The operating frequency of the transmitter is approximately 1.4kHz.

The receiver circuit appears in Figure 2.9. The output from the phototransistor (TR1) is coupled by C3 to a high gain common emitter amplifier based on TR2. C4 couples the output from this stage to a half-wave rectifier and smoothing network which uses D2 and D3 in a conventional configuration. The electronic switch is a simple common emitter type (TR3). Provided a reasonably strong positive bias is produced by the

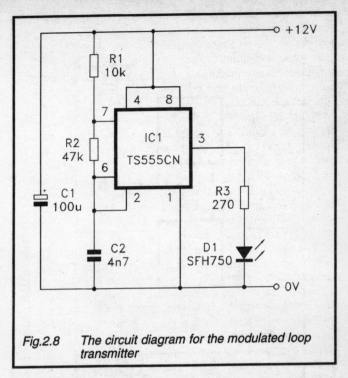

*Fig.2.8   The circuit diagram for the modulated loop
transmitter*

smoothing circuit, TR3 will be switched on, and its collector
potential will be no more than a few tens of millivolts. This
holds the alarm generator in the off state. If the signal from the
transmitter ceases, the charge on C5 rapidly subsides, and TR3
switches off. R7 then pulls the reset input of IC2 high, and the
alarm sounds.

The current consumption of the entire unit is about 17 to 20
milliamps. A high capacity battery supply or rechargeable
batteries could be used if portable operation is required.
Otherwise, a mains power supply unit is a more practical
choice. The low power mains power supply described in
Chapter 1 is suitable, as is any mains power supply which can
provide a reasonably stable and well smoothed 12 volts. Note
that this circuit is sensitive to "hum" and other noise on the
supply lines, and is unlikely to work if the supply has anything

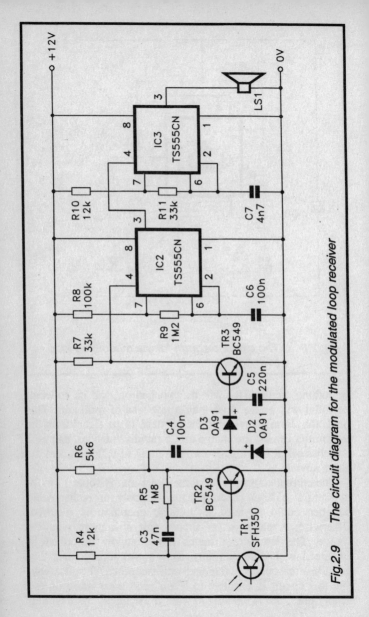

Fig.2.9   The circuit diagram for the modulated loop receiver

88

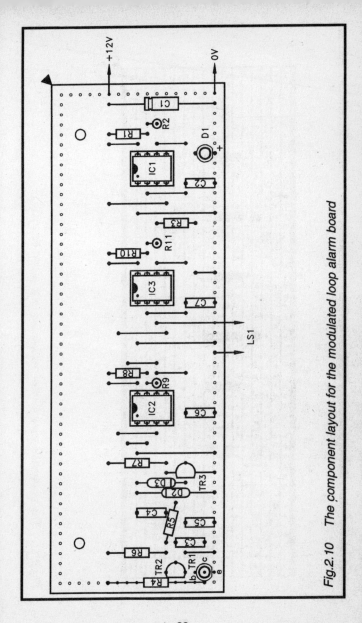

Fig.2.10   The component layout for the modulated loop alarm board

89

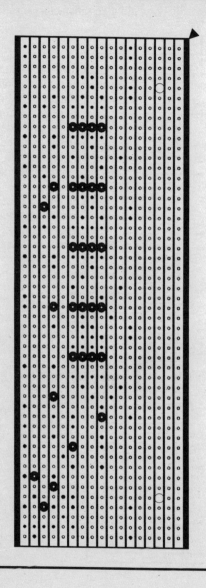

Fig.2.11   The underside view for the modulated loop alarm board

other than a very low ripple content. It is highly unlikely that a simple unregulated supply would give satisfactory results.

Construction

Details of the stripboard for the modulated loop alarm are provided in Figures 2.10 (component side view) and 2.11 (underside view). The board measures 50 holes by 17 copper strips. Construction of the unit should be quite straightforward, but bear in mind that D2 and D3 are germanium diodes, and that they are more vulnerable to heat damage than the more familiar silicon diodes. It should not be necessary to use a heatshunt when connecting them, but the iron should be applied to the joints for no more than a second or two.

There are one or two breaks in the copper strips and a couple of link-wires which seem to serve no useful purpose, but these help to minimise breakthrough from the transmitter to the receiver. This breakthrough must be kept down to a very low level or the alarm will be held in the "off" state. The notes on fibre-optics provided previously apply equally to this project, and will not be repeated here.

The prototype worked well using a 20 metre length of fibre-optic cable, which should be more than adequate for most purposes. TR1 should not be subjected to strong mains powered lighting, as the modulation on such lighting could hold the alarm in the "off" state. In most instances the case will provide more than ample shielding to prevent this problem.

Components for Figures 2.8 and 2.9

Resistors (all 0.25 watt 5% carbon film)

R1	10k
R2	47k
R3	270R
R4	12k
R5	1M8
R6	5k6
R7	33k
R8	100k
R9	1M2

R10	12k
R11	33k

Capacitors

C1	100µ 16V elect
C2	4n7 polyester
C3	47n polyester
C4	100n polyester
C5	220n polyester
C6	100n polyester
C7	4n7 polyester

Semiconductors

IC1	TS555CN or similar
IC2	TS555CN or similar
IC3	TS555CN or similar
TR1	SFH350
TR2	BC549
TR3	BC549
D1	SFH750
D2	OA91
D3	OA91

Miscellaneous

LS1	Cased ceramic resonator

Case, stripboard measuring 50 holes by 17 copper strips, fibre-optic cable, 8-pin DIL holder (3 off), wire, solder, etc.

Window Alarm

This unit is primarily intended as a sensor for a switch activated alarm system, but it can be used as a stand-alone alarm if preferred. It makes use of ultrasonic soundwaves, which are sounds that are too high in pitch for human hearing to sense. In other words, sounds at frequencies of about 20kHz or more.

There are two normal ways of using ultrasonics in burglar alarms. The unit featured here is the more simple type, and it is a form of passive alarm. It is designed to detect the sound from a breaking window if someone tries this method of forced entry. Obviously an intruder will not necessarily try this method of entry, and I would certainly not recommend this type of alarm for use as the sole type of sensor in an alarm system. Also, the unit is too limited in its capabilities to operate effectively as a stand-alone alarm system with no other alarm system in use. It is much better suited to being part of a switch type burglar alarm, acting as one of the extra sensors. For example, a couple of alarms of this type plus a few switch mats could be used as the normally-open sensor switches, with door and window switches used for the normally-closed sensor switches.

An advantage of this type of sensor is that it can give early triggering of the system. Many types of alarm only operate once someone has actually entered the premises, whereas this type of alarm, if the right type of entry is tried, will trigger while someone is still trying to gain entry.

Of course, as explained in chapter one, there is an alternative form of broken window alarm which utilizes fine wire or metal foil fitted in or on the windows. The idea here is that the wire or foil breaks if the window is smashed. This enables these window sensors to be wired into a system and used just like ordinary normally-closed door and window switches. Although a very simple and effective system, not everyone is prepared to put up with the wire or foil on or in their windows, and the presence of this type of sensor is usually quite obvious. This factor is something that varies from one make of sensor to another, and some of the more sophisticated (and expensive types) are much more discreet about their presence. Most sensors of this type are readily detectable though, which makes them potentially less effective than an unseen system.

Why Ultrasonics?
On the face of it there is little point in using an ultrasonic detector in an alarm of this type. When a window is broken, even if steps are taken to deaden the sound, there is still quite a loud noise which includes a strong audio frequency content. An audio sound detector would seem to offer a perfectly good alternative, with a level of sensitivity that would probably be well in excess of that provided by an ultrasonic system.

As with virtually all burglar alarm sensors, it is not just a matter of detecting an intruder, it is also a matter of avoiding false alarms. In this respect a sensitive audio frequency sound switch is very vulnerable. Anyone in the vicinity of the detector would be likely to trigger it, although this would not matter if the system is only going to be used when the premises are unoccupied. However, there are plenty of sounds in the average environment that could easily result in spurious triggering.

Thunder and lightning can cause problems with any burglar alarm system, mainly due to electrical pick up of the strong signal generated by lightning. With a sound activated alarm it would obviously be the sound of the thunder that would represent the greatest threat of false alarms. In fact any moderately loud rumble of thunder would certainly trigger the system, and this factor alone renders an ordinary sound activated switch of limited practical use in this application. There are plenty of other sounds which could trigger such a system, including low flying aircraft, or the sound of the wind when conditions are stormy.

A system which is only sensitive to ultrasonic sound waves offers greatly improved immunity to false alarms. Thunder, aircraft noise, and gale force winds produce what is predominantly low frequency sound. Even if a strong source of ultrasonic sound should pass by outside (a bat perhaps), it is still unlikely to trigger the alarm. One reason for this is that sounds at ultrasonic frequencies tend to be absorbed by air, which limits the range from which the system can be triggered. This has an attendant disadvantage in that it limits the range at which the alarm can detect a window being broken. This is not a very large drawback though, since there would normally be no need to have the sensor more than a metre or two from the monitored window. The second reason for external sources of ultrasonic sound failing to trigger the unit is that high frequency sounds are not very good at passing through solid objects. Even something like a thin pane of glass will block quite strong ultrasonic sounds, which contrasts with low frequency sounds that can even pass through quite thick walls with a relatively low degree of attenuation.

System Operation
The block diagram of Figure 2.12 shows the arrangement used in the breaking window alarm. A microphone is used at the

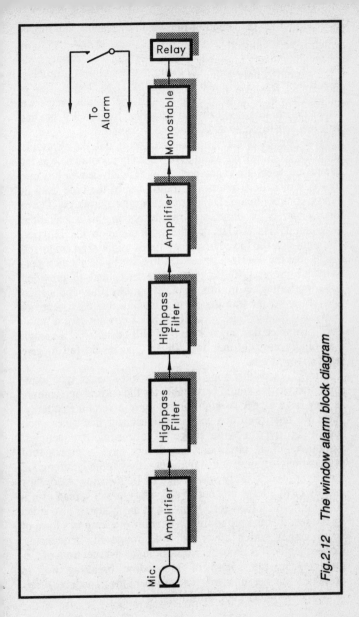

Fig.2.12 The window alarm block diagram

input to pick up the sound of the window breaking, but this is not an ordinary microphone. Microphone inserts, such as crystal, electret, and dynamic types, offer good sensitivity over the audio frequency range, but their response almost invariably falls away very rapidly above about 15kHz to 20kHz. This is the opposite of what we require for this application, where we need a system that is sensitive at ultrasonic frequencies, but has very low sensitivity to audio frequency sounds.

Microphones which have good sensitivity into the ultrasonic range are produced, but seem to be virtually unobtainable as far as amateur users are concerned. This basically leaves just one choice, which is an ultrasonic transducer of the type used in remote control circuits, Doppler shift burglar alarms, etc. I have tried a variety of ultrasonic transducers in this application, including 25kHz, 32kHz, and the more common 40kHz types. I thought that the lower frequency types might offer improved results, but the 40kHz type seemed to offer by far the best performance. Several 40kHz types were tried, and all provided good performance in this application. As this application involves using the transducers in a manner that they were not really designed to cope with, obviously I can not give a "cast-iron" guarantee that any 40kHz type will be suitable, although it is highly unlikely that any 40kHz type would fail to give satisfactory results.

It might seem that none of these remote-control type ultrasonic transducers would be suitable for the current application, as they have a peak of high sensitivity at a certain frequency. What we require in this case is a transducer that gives good sensitivity over a wide range of ultrasonic frequencies. Although 40kHz ultrasonic transducers have a pronounced peak in their response at this frequency, they actually offer good sensitivity over a fairly wide range of frequencies. Also, they usually have a large number of secondary peaks spread over a wide range of frequencies. Operation of the system is also aided by the fact that the sound from a window breaking is a form of noise signal which covers a wide range of frequencies. Consequently, it is probably impossible for the spectrum of frequencies in the sound of a window breaking not to produce some output at frequencies where the transducer offers at least moderately good sensitivity.

The output level of the transducer is not likely to be very large, and may well be less than 1 millivolt r.m.s. A pre-amplifier is therefore used to boost the signal to a more usable level. This is followed by two highpass filters which give a combined attenuation rate of 36dB per octave. These might seem to be superfluous, but as pointed out previously, ultrasonic transducers actually cover a broad frequency range. They are quite sensitive over the upper audio range, and the highpass filters are needed to reduce this sensitivity to an acceptable level.

The output level from the filters is still quite low in amplitude, and a second amplifier stage is used to boost the signal to a more useful level of a few volts peak-to-peak. The output of the second amplifier feeds into a monostable multivibrator, and this is triggered by negative input pulses. Normally the output of the second amplifier is static at a voltage that is too high to trigger the monostable. When the unit is activated, the amplifier is driven to the point where the output signal is clipped, or nearly so, and on the first negative going half cycle the monostable is triggered. The monostable directly drives a relay, which is turned on for about one second when the alarm is activated. This should be long enough to reliably set off the main alarm, but the output pulse duration is easily altered if necessary. A pair of normally-open relay contacts are connected into the main alarm system, or normally-closed contacts can be used if the relay is suitably equipped.

The Circuit

Figure 2.13 shows the main circuit diagram for the breaking window alarm, but the output circuitry is shown separately in Figure 2.14.

An ultrasonic transducer is a ceramic device, rather like a crystal microphone. It has a very high resistance, and can therefore be coupled direct to the input of the first amplifier stage without any need for a d.c. blocking capacitor. The first amplifier stage is a two transistor circuit which has TR1 as a high gain common emitter voltage amplifier, and TR2 as an emitter follower buffer stage. The latter provides a low output impedance so that the unit can drive the filter stages properly. The filters are both conventional third order (18dB per octave)

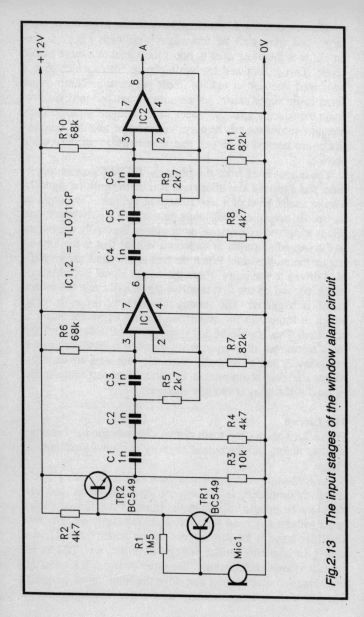

Fig.2.13   The input stages of the window alarm circuit

98

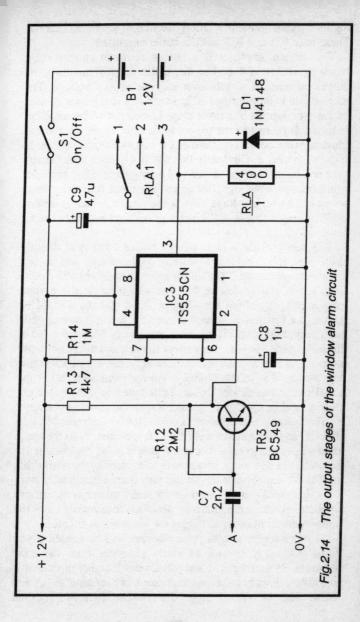

Fig.2.14   The output stages of the window alarm circuit

highpass types, having a cutoff frequency at around 25kHz. These have IC1 and IC2 as their buffer amplifiers.

The second amplifier is a simple common emitter stage based on TR3. It is biased so that under standby conditions its output potential is a little over half the supply voltage. The monostable is built around IC3, which is a low power version of the ever popular 555 timer chip. The output of the amplifier is connected direct to the trigger input of IC3 (pin 2), and this must be taken below one third of the supply voltage in order to trigger the device. Obviously this will not happen under quiescent conditions, but the device will be triggered if the amplifier produces an output signal of more than about four volts peak-to-peak. The high voltage gain of the circuit, which is around 90dB, ensures that it will always provide an adequate output level.

IC3 can provide a high enough output current to directly drive any relay having a suitable coil voltage and a coil resistance of around 270 ohms or more. A standard 555 can be used for IC1 if preferred, but this will increase the current consumption by about 8 milliamps. Note that the TS555CN, although a low power version of the 555, can still source quite high output currents. Some other low power 555s have rather limited source and (or) sink current figures, and might not work properly in this application. Accordingly, the use of substitute low power 555s in this circuit is not recommended. D1 is the usual protection diode. Do not be tempted to omit this component, and be careful to connect it with the correct polarity.

The output pulse duration is controlled by the values of R14 and C8, and is approximately 1.1 C R seconds. With the specified values this gives a theoretical output pulse duration of 1.1 seconds, but due to the component tolerances (particularly that of C8) the actual pulse length can vary quite substantially from the calculated figure. This does not really matter in the current application where the unit only needs to momentarily close the relay contacts in order to trigger the main alarm circuit.

A much longer output pulse duration will be needed if you wish to directly control an alarm generator from the relay contacts. By making R14 and (or) C8 much higher in value it is possible to greatly increase the duration of the output pulse, and pulse times of a few minutes are possible. Bear in mind that very high timing resistances and capacitances might not work properly. Very high value capacitors tend to have significant leakage currents, and a resistor of a few megohms in value will provide a charge current of only around one or two microamps. It is quite possible that the leakage current will be equal to or greater than the charge current, so that the charge voltage never reaches the two thirds of the supply voltage threshold level at which the output pulse is terminated. This will not prevent the alarm from sounding, but it would prevent an automatic switch-off from being obtained. In a less severe case the automatic switch-off might be obtained, but the output pulse duration would be greatly extended.

If you require a long output pulse length, use a good quality capacitor for C8 such as a low leakage miniature electrolytic, or better still, a tantalum "bead" capacitor. Suitable values for R14 and C8 are 5M6 and 47µ respectively. With such a high value for R14 it is essential for C8 to be a very high quality type such as a tantalum capacitor.

The quiescent current consumption of the circuit is about 3.5 milliamps, and about ten times this figure for the short period that the relay is activated. It is possible to use high capacity primary cells as the power source, but rechargeable batteries are probably a more economic way of powering the circuit. It might be possible to power the unit from the main alarm circuit if this has a reasonably well smoothed and regulated 12 volt supply and sufficient spare output current. Alternatively, the unit could have its own built-in mains power supply unit. The low power supply described in chapter one is suitable.

With a project of this type there is some advantage in using a battery supply. The circuit is extremely sensitive, has a wide bandwidth, and is consequently vulnerable to spurious triggering due to stray pick up of electrical noise. If the unit is battery powered and housed in a metal case (to provide overall screening), any stray pick up is likely to be too weak to cause spurious triggering. With a mains powered unit it can be very difficult to effectively screen the circuit from the power supply section, and there is also a potential problem with noise spikes being coupled into the unit directly via the power supply circuit. The main circuit and the power supply wiring should be kept as far apart as possible.

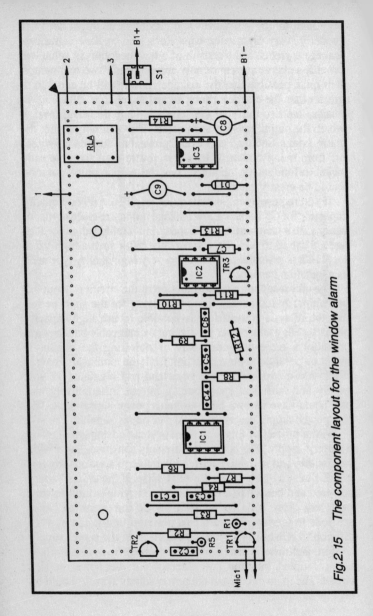

Fig.2.15   The component layout for the window alarm

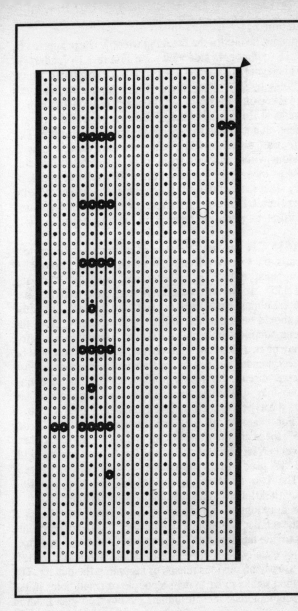

Fig.2.16 The underside view of the window alarm board

Construction

The stripboard layout for the breaking window alarm appears in Figure 2.15 (component side view) and Figure 2.16 (underside view). This layout is based on a 0.1 inch pitch stripboard which has 50 holes by 21 copper strips. The components are quite densely packed on parts of the circuit board, but construction of the board is still reasonably easy. However, I would strongly recommend that you use the specified types of capacitor. The mylar types are small printed circuit mounting capacitors with long leadout wires, enabling them to be easily fitted into this layout. Most other types will not fit into the available space, or have very short leadout wires that could make it difficult to wire them into circuit. However, miniature polyester layer capacitors of five millimetre pitch can be used for the filter capacitors (C1 to C6).

The TS555CN has very effective built-in anti-static protection circuits, but I would still recommend the use of a holder for this component (which is rather more expensive than the standard 555). If the ultrasonic transducer used for Mic1 has one of its terminals in electrical contact with the case, this is the one that should be connected to the negative supply rail of the unit. Some suppliers only sell ultrasonic transducers in pairs. These may be two identical components, but often there will be one device intended for use in the transmitter, and one for use in a receiver circuit. Obviously in this case it is the receiving transducer that should be used. If the two transducers are different, the type numbers normally make it clear which is which. For example, if they are numbered "T40-16" and "R40-16", these are the transmitting and receiving transducers respectively. A lot of transducers have this form of coding, with "T" and "R" used to indicate transmitter and receiver respectively. The two numbers following this are the operating frequency (in kilohertz) and the diameter (in millimetres).

If the markings do not make it clear which transducer is which, the retailer's catalogue or data sheet for the components should provide the necessary information. Ultrasonic transducers do not usually have provision for screw mounting. In fact there is usually no obvious means of mounting them at all. The best method seems to be to drill a couple of small holes in the case to accommodate their terminals, and to then glue them in place using a good quality gap-filling adhesive such as an epoxy resin type.

The unit should operate with any 12 volt relay which has a coil resistance of about 270 ohms or more, plus contacts of suitable rating and the type you require. However, relays other than the specified type (or an exact equivalent) will not fit into this stripboard layout, and may have to be mounted off-board. The specified relay is a miniature type which has a 12 volt 400 ohm coil and a single changeover contact. The contacts have a current rating of two amps (one amp with inductive loads), and maximum voltage ratings of 24 volts d.c. and 120 volts a.c. By using the "pole" contact and one of the other two contacts, a changeover contact can provide normally-open or normally closed operation. For normally closed operation use points "1" and "3". Normally open operation is achieved by connecting points "2" and "3" to the main alarm circuit.

The nature of this type of alarm is such that there is probably no point in going to the bother of fitting it in an extremely tough case and using a key-switch as the on/off switch. If it has not gone off by the time an intruder has actually gained entry into the premises, then it will presumably not go off at all (unless they break a window to get out)!

No problems with acoustic feedback causing oscillation were experienced with the prototype, but there is a slight risk of this occurring. The sound of the relay switching off can retrigger the unit. In order to minimise the risk of problems with acoustic feedback it is probably as well to have the ultrasonic transducer and the relay positioned at opposite ends of the case.

Testing
One way of testing the unit is to smash some glass one or two metres in front of the transducer. Smashing glass is a little risky though, even if you do take the necessary safety precautions such as wearing gloves and goggles. It is not really necessary to use breaking glass to test the unit anyway, since any source of ultrasonic sound should activate the unit. It would be possible to electronically generate a suitable test signal, but there is a far more simple solution. I found that simply rubbing ones fingers together about 200 millimetres or so in front of the transducer produced sufficient ultrasonic sound to trigger the unit!

When installing the unit bear in mind that it can not be guaranteed to have an operating range of more than about three metres. It must therefore be installed reasonably close to the window it is monitoring, but presumably there will not be a dire need to have the unit further away from the window than this anyway. Ultrasonic sound waves are highly directional, and the "angle of view" of most ultrasonic transducers is quite narrow (around plus and minus 15 degrees). The transducer should therefore be aimed reasonably accurately at the window, and far enough back to give an adequate area of coverage. With large windows best results might be obtained with the unit mounted to one side of the window and aimed at an angle across it. This should bring virtually the whole of the window within the unit's "view", without any part of the window going out of range. The sensor can be mounted actually on the window, which would presumably give excellent results. On the other hand, it might give away the presence of the alarm, and it is not my preferred way of doing things.

Units of this type are reasonably free from problems with false alarms, but they are not completely immune to them. There are possible sources of ultrasonic sounds in the home, such as television sets, but if the alarm is only used when people are out of the house, or in bed asleep, these are unlikely to cause any problems. Apparently it is important that when a window has been smashed, all the chips of glass should be removed before the new pane of glass is fitted. It seems that there is otherwise a risk of the wind vibrating the window, which in turn vibrates the tiny chips of glass. These can produce sufficient ultrasonic sound to trigger an alarm of this type!

Note that the unit will probably trigger at switch-on, as it takes a fraction of a second before the circuit settles down with all the voltages at their normal quiescent levels. This will not usually matter, since the exit delay of the main alarm will prevent this spurious signal from triggering the main alarm. It might be a severe problem if the unit is used to directly control an alarm generator. If this unwanted triggering should prove to be a problem, all that is needed are a couple of extra components, as shown in Figure 2.17. This is just a simple C – R timing circuit which holds IC3 in the reset state for a short time

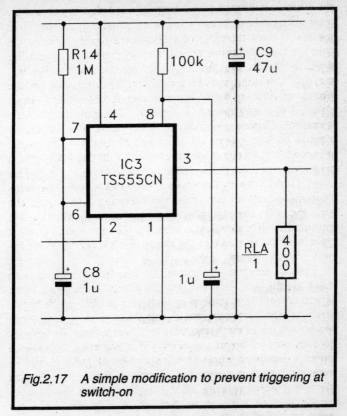

Fig.2.17   A simple modification to prevent triggering at switch-on

after switch-on, so that it can not be triggered in this period. If the alarm triggers at switch-on, and the relay remains closed, assuming that there are no constructional errors, the most likely cause is that the bias voltage at TR3's collector is too low. This can be rectified by making R14 a little higher in value (2M7 should suffice).

Components for Figures 2.13 and 2.14

Resistors (all ¼ watt 5%)
R1   1M5
R2   4k7

R3	10k
R4	4k7
R5	2k7
R6	68k
R7	82k
R8	4k7
R9	2k7
R10	68k
R11	82k
R12	2M2
R13	4k7
R14	1M

Capacitors

C1 – C6	1n mylar or 5mm pitch polyester
C7	2n2 mylar
C8	1µ 63V radial elect
C9	47µ 16V axial elect

Semiconductors

IC1	TLO71CP or similar
IC2	TLO71CP or similar
IC3	TS555CN
TR1	BC549
TR2	BC549
TR3	BC549
D1	1N4148

Miscellaneous

Mic1	40kHz ultrasonic transducer (see text)
S1	SPST miniature toggle switch
B1	12 volt (e.g. 8 × AA cells in holder)
RLA/1	12 volt 400R coil, single changeover contact (Maplin YX94C or similar, see text)

Case, 0.1 inch pitch stripboard having 50 holes by 21 copper strips, 8-pin d.i.l. holder (3 off), wire, battery connector, solder, etc.

Passive IR Detector

At one time passive infra-red senors were very expensive components that were only available to professional users. These days they are available from several amateur electronics suppliers at quite reasonable prices. They are certainly one of the more interesting types of electronic sensor, and they have a number of practical security applications including burglar alarms, automatic doors, and automatic lighting. The unit featured here is a sensor for a switch activated burglar alarm.

It would perhaps be as well to start with an explanation of exactly what is meant by a "passive" infra-red detector. This is a device which detects an infra-red source of some kind, but in all common applications the source is a person. In other words, the circuit detects the body heat of someone within its field of "view", and the circuit then activates an alarm, switches on the lighting, or whatever. A passive system does not transmit any infra-red, and relies on sufficient infra-red being provided by the objects which must be detected.

An advantage of a passive system is that it will readily detect people, because they generate large amounts of heat which makes them an easy "target". Many potential sources of spurious triggering, such as moths and other flying insects, do not provide sufficient heat to trigger a passive infra-red detector. Provided the system is installed and used sensibly, this gives what is usually excellent reliability with very few false alarms.

Normal semiconductor infra-red devices operate in the part of the infra-red spectrum that is close to the visible red wavelengths. In other words, at wavelengths of around 850 to 950µm. These are virtually useless for passive infra-red detection, where wavelengths of around 1 to 20µm are involved. Devices designed specifically for this application are needed in order to obtain really good results. These devices have little in common with phototransistors and photodiodes, and they are not actually semiconductors.

They are ceramic components made from a substance such as lead zirconate titanate, and they consists of a slice of the material with electrodes on opposite faces. When subjected to heating the device produces opposite electrical charges on the two electrodes. This effect is similar to the more familiar piezo electric effect which is utilized in such things as crystal microphones and ceramic pick-ups. The piezo effect generates a similar electrical signal as a result of physical distortion. Like the output from a ceramic pick-up, the output from a passive infra-red sensor, or "pyro" sensor as they are usually called, is at a high impedance.

Practical pyro sensors normally consist of more than just the sensing element, and in most cases an integral Jfet source follower buffer stage is included. Most pyro sensors have twin sensing elements. Figures 2.18(a) and (b) respectively show the circuits for single and twin element pyro sensors. In both cases Ra is the gate bias resistor and Rb is the source load resistor. The source load resistor is not always included in the sensor, and with some sensors a discrete load resistor is therefore needed.

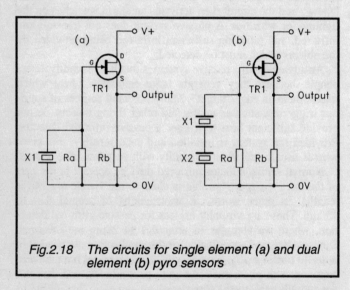

Fig.2.18   The circuits for single element (a) and dual element (b) pyro sensors

The twin element sensors have the two elements wired out-of-phase, which would seem to be a good way of obtaining no output signal! The background infra-red level does indeed produce zero output from the sensor, with the signal from one element cancelling out the signal from the other. This lack of response to the background signal, and to changes in the

110

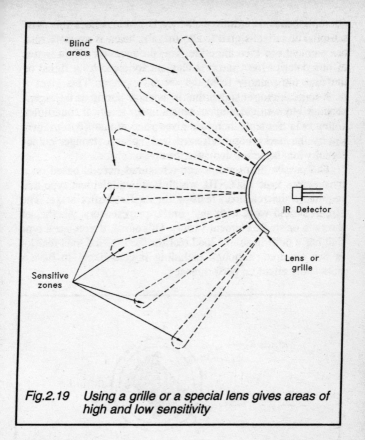

Fig.2.19 *Using a grille or a special lens gives areas of high and low sensitivity*

background level, is the main reason for using twin sensors. Although the sensor ignores the background infra-red signal, it will still respond properly when someone comes within the area it covers. The important point to bear in mind here is that this type of sensor is designed to detect someone moving within its field of "view", and that it is not designed to detect a stationary infra-red source.

In use a special lens or a simple grille is used in front of the sensor. This gives it zones of high and low sensitivity (Figure 2.19). As someone moves across the sensor's field of view they pass from a "blind spot" to an area of high sensitivity. As they do so, a beam of infra-red energy is swept across the pyro sensor. The latter is oriented so that the beam is swept across one element and then the other. This produces an output signal of one polarity from the first element followed by a signal of the opposite polarity from the second element. This gives a peak-to-peak output signal that is twice as strong as the signal produced by a single element sensor under identical conditions. Using twin elements therefore gives good immunity to triggering by the background infra-red level, plus a stronger output signal when someone activates the sensor.

The passive infra-red detector featured here is based on a pyro sensor type E600ST0, which is a dual element type that requires a discrete load resistor for its Jfet buffer stage. The circuit should work with any similar pyro sensors, whether of the twin or single element variety. Of course, if you use a type that has a built-in source load resistor the external load resistor is not required, although including it is unlikely to have a noticeable effect on performance.

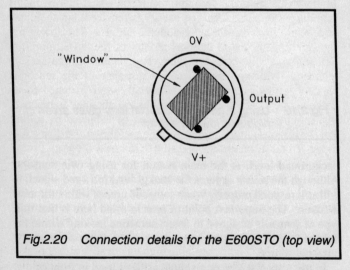

Fig.2.20   Connection details for the E600STO (top view)

Connection details for the E600ST0 are provided in Figure 2.20, which is a top view. This device is housed in a metal encapsulation that is similar to the standard TO5 type used for

112

many transistors, thyristors, etc. There is a rectangular window in the top of the case, and in use the device must be positioned so that this is horizontal. If the window is vertical, the twin elements will receive the beams of infra-red energy more or less simultaneously, and there will be little change in the output voltage from the sensor.

System Operation

The block diagram of Figure 2.21 helps to explain the way in which the unit functions. The output signal from the sensor is likely to be very small, and would normally be just a few millivolts peak-to-peak. A large amount of amplification is needed in order to bring the signal to a level that will reliably operate a relay driver stage. In this case the amplification is provided by a two stage amplifier.

The output signal from the pyro sensor is predominantly at frequencies of around 0.5 to 2Hz. The sensing elements in the pyro device are made very thin so that they heat up reasonably rapidly when some infra-red energy is received, but the upper frequency limit is still only about 2 or 3Hz. The lower frequency limit is due to the bias resistor of the buffer amplifier leaking away the electrical charges generated by the sensing elements. Although the frequency response of the sensor is strictly limited, its response is actually well matched to its intended application, and good results are obtained in practice. An improved signal-to-noise ratio can be achieved by rolling off the response of the circuit at frequencies of more than a few hertz. This is achieved using a simple lowpass filter.

A level detector is fed with the output signal from the second amplifier stage. Normally the output of the level detector is low, but it will go high if the output potential from the amplifier drops below a certain threshold level. The output voltage of the amplifier varies between virtually the full supply potentials when the unit is activated, and this results in the output of the level detector going high on negative signal peaks. This activates the relay via a simple relay driver circuit, and the relay contacts then activate the main alarm.

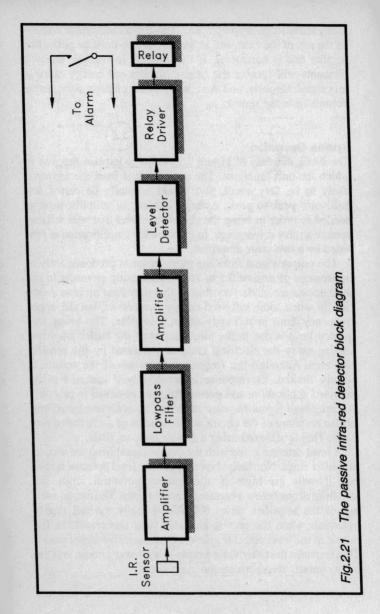

Fig.2.21   The passive infra-red detector block diagram

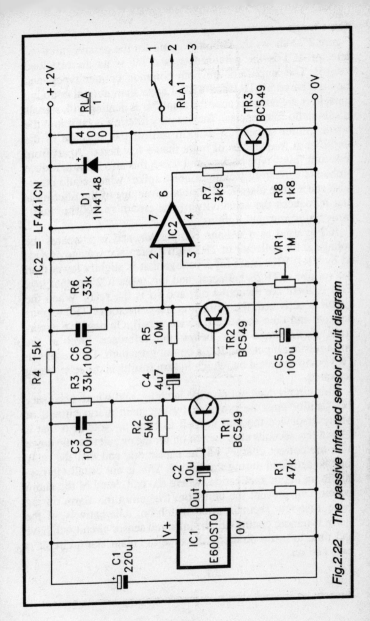

Fig.2.22 The passive infra-red sensor circuit diagram

The Circuit

Figure 2.22 shows the circuit diagram for the passive infra-red detector. IC1 is the pyro sensor, and R1 is its discrete load resistor. The amplifiers are both common emitter types, and they are based on TR1 and TR2. Larger than normal coupling capacitors are used because the amplifier is dealing with signals at sub-audio frequencies. The lowpass filtering is built into the two amplifier stages. C3 and C6 roll-off the response of the amplifier at frequencies of more than a few hertz. Apart from reducing "hiss" type background noise, this also helps to reduce problems with stray pickup of noise spikes which could otherwise cause false alarms. A further advantage of the filtering is that it reduces the sensitivity of the circuit to 100Hz "hum" from mains powered lighting.

IC2 is used as a voltage comparator, and it compares the voltage at the collector of TR2 with a reference voltage provided by VR1. VR1 is set for a voltage that is slightly lower than the voltage at TR2's collector, and this takes IC2's output low. TR3 is therefore switched off, and so is the relay. When the circuit is activated, the voltage at the collector of TR2 swings positive and then negative (or vice versa). On negative excursions this voltage goes below the reference level at the non-inverting input, and IC2's output goes high. This results in TR3 being switched on, which in turn results in the relay being activated.

This circuit does not provide latching, and where necessary this facility must be provided by the main alarm circuit, or whatever device the unit is used to control. Note also that it takes a few seconds after switch-on for the circuit to settle down with the correct charges on the capacitors, and that the relay may be activated during this period. This is not usually important in an alarm application, where the exit delay of the alarm system will prevent the unit from triggering the alarm during these first few seconds after switch-on. Alternatively, if the alarm is remote controlled, the infra-red sensor circuit will have had time to settle down by the time the main alarm circuit is switched on.

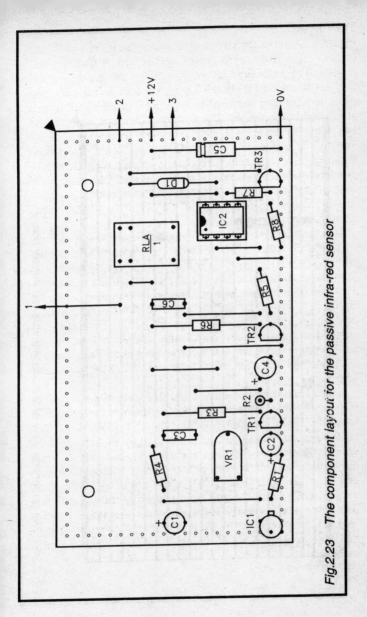

Fig.2.23   The component layout for the passive infra-red sensor

117

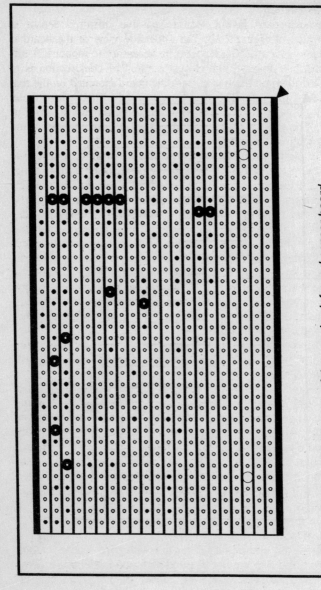

Fig.2.24 The underside view of the passive infra-red sensor board

118

Construction

The stripboard layout for the passive infra-red sensor is provided in Figure 2.23. The underside view of the board is shown in Figure 2.24. It might be necessary to mount IC1 off-board, but probably the easiest method of construction is to have it fitted on the board, with the board mounted on the rear panel of the case. The front panel is then fitted with a hole, grille, or lens at the appropriate position, directly in front of IC1. The subject of lenses and grilles is fully covered in the next section incidentally.

Be careful to fit IC1 correctly. The arc of three connections has the 0 volt lead at the bottom, the positive supply lead at the top, and the output lead in the middle. This should bring IC1's window into a more or less horizontal position, but it might be necessary to twist the body of the component slightly in order to get its orientation absolutely right. This is not really essential though, since a small error here will not significantly affect sensitivity. Try not to touch IC1's window as this could impair the sensitivity of the unit. Apparently, touching the window can make it less transparent to long wavelength infra-red energy, even though there may be little obvious effect at visible light wavelengths. If the window should become finger-marked, clean it gently with a soft cloth.

The comments about the relay for the window alarm (see page 105) apply equally to this project. Consequently, they will not be repeated here.

Giving VR1 a suitable setting is very straightforward. Start with VR1's wiper well towards the positive supply end of the track. This should result in the relay switching on. The relay should switch off at some point if VR1's wiper is gradually moved down towards the opposite end of the track. It is probably best to move the wiper a bit further down the track from this point. Doing so will give a slight reduction in sensitivity, but it will greatly reduce the risk of false alarms due to noise, drift, etc.

Optical system

Obtaining the special lenses for use with pyro sensors can be difficult, and they are not likely to be found in electronic components catalogues. However, lenses of this type can be obtained from specialist suppliers (see components list). It has to be pointed out that lenses for use at visible light wavelengths, or even the shorter infra-red wavelengths, are usually of no use at all with pyro sensors. Most ordinary plastic and glass lenses seem to be virtually opaque to long wavelength infra-red! If you can obtain a proper lens for use with a pyro sensor, then it should work well with this system provided it is used in accordance with the manufacturers or retailers recommendations.

I have obtained good results using the Chartland Electronics lens type CE24. It is a rectangular lens which must be mounted with an orientation that matches that of the "window" in the pyro sensor (i.e. horizontally). The lens is flat as supplied, and it must be fitted onto the front of the case via a mounting that gives it a curve with a radius of 29 to 30 millimetres. Gluing the lens in place via something like balsa wood top and bottom pieces having the appropriate curve is all that is needed. Use a reasonably thick sheet material for the top and bottom pieces so that the finished assembly is reasonably strong. A thickness of around four or five millimetres seems to be best. Note that the adhesive used must be a type that is suitable for use with soft plastics. The pyro sensor is mounted 29 to 30 millimetres behind the centre of the lens.

Using a simple grille is the main alternative to using a lens. The E600ST0 has an angle of view of 40 degrees. A lens system can increase the effective field of view, but with a grille the coverage of the system can be no wider than the response angle of the sensor. However, for most applications a 40 degree field of coverage is adequate. A grille is easily made from a piece of plastic or aluminium. Simply cut some vertical slits in a small sheet of the material, and curve it through about 45 degrees. You may like to experiment with the sensor-to-grille distance, and with grilles having slits of various widths. My experiments would suggest that neither of these factors are particularly critical.

In fact the unit will work quite well if IC1 "looks" through a hole of about five to seven millimetres in diameter drilled in the front panel of the case. This gives just one zone of high sensitivity, but this is usually sufficient provided the unit is aimed sensibly.

A grille or single hole offer simple and inexpensive solutions to the problem, but both methods have a serious drawback. This is simply that a lens gives a much greater operating range. An operating range of 10 metres or more over a very wide angle can be achieved using a good quality lens such as the CE24. Using a grille the maximum range is likely to be no more than three metres. Clearly this is still perfectly adequate for many applications. An advantage of the lower sensitivity provided by a grille is that the system is less prone to problems with false alarms. Using a very high level of sensitivity makes the system prone to spurious triggering due to air turbulence. Even using a grille, the unit should not be installed so that it is aimed at a radiator, or any obvious source of infra-red that could produce spurious triggering.

Components for Figure 2.22

Resistors (all 0.25 watt 5% carbon film)

R1	47k
R2	5M6
R3	33k
R4	15k
R5	10M
R6	33k
R7	3k9
R8	1k8

Potentiometer

VR1	1M min hor preset

Capacitors

C1	220µ 16V elect
C2	10µ 25V elect
C3	100n polyester
C4	4µ7 50V elect
C5	100µ 16V elect
C6	100n polyester

Semiconductors

IC1	E600ST0 pyro sensor (or similar)
IC2	LF441CN

TR1	BC549
TR2	BC549
TR3	BC549
D1	1N4148

Miscellaneous
RLA/1   12 volt 400R coil, single changeover contact (see text)

Case, 0.1 inch pitch stripboard measuring 37 holes by 21 copper strips, 8-pin DIL holder, wire, solder, etc.

The lens type CE24 is available from Chartland Electronics Ltd., Chartland House, Old Station Approach, Randalls Road, Leatherhead, Surrey, KT22 7TE (Tel: 01372 363666). Chartland Electronics can also supply suitable pyro sensors for this project, such as the SBA02. Note that the Chartland pyro sensors have built-in source resistors, and do not therefore require a discrete load resistor (R1 in this circuit).

Doppler Shift Alarm
This is another alarm sensor that makes use of ultrasonic sound waves. However, unlike the window alarm described previously, this Doppler shift system is an active sensor which generates the ultrasonic sound that it detects. It is intended as a backup to the alarm system's sensor switches, and it will detect someone who has managed to enter the protected premises without activating the alarm.

Probably most readers will be familiar with the term "Doppler shift". This is the apparent shift in frequency that occurs when some form of energy waves are emitted from a moving object. If the object is coming towards you, any waves it sends out will appear to be at a higher frequency than they actually are. Conversely, if the object is moving away from you, the apparent frequency of an emitted signal will be lower than its true frequency. This effect is demonstrated by a fast car which passes by while sounding its horn. There is a sudden and very noticeable drop in the pitch of the horn's note as the car passes by.

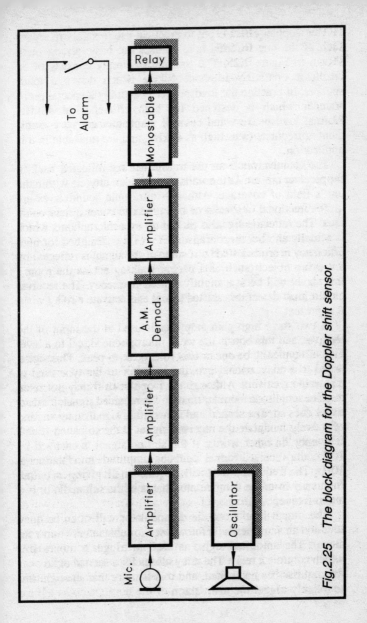

Fig.2.25 The block diagram for the Doppler shift sensor

The Doppler effect is put to practical use in an alarm sensor such as the one featured here. It uses the basic arrangement shown in Figure 2.25. The transmitter simply consists of an oscillator operating at about 40kHz which drives a loudspeaker. In practice the loudspeaker is actually a special piezo sounder which is designed for high efficiency at 40kHz. Normal loudspeakers and ceramic resonators are very inefficient at frequencies as high as 40kHz, and are unusable in this application.

The soundwaves from the transmitter are reflected back to the receiver circuit via the walls, furniture, or anyone within the unit's field of coverage. Although ultrasonic soundwaves are quite directional, a system of this type can cover a reasonable area. The reflected signal is picked up by a microphone, which is actually another piezo transducer which is designed for high efficiency at around 40kHz. If some of the signal is reflected by a moving object (such as a person walking across the room), this signal will be at a slightly shifted frequency. The receiver circuit must detect this shifted signal and activate a relay when it is present.

A two stage high gain amplifier is used at the input of the receiver, and this boosts the weak microphone signal to a level that will typically be one or two volts peak-to-peak. This signal is fed to a conventional a.m. demodulator of the type used in a.m. radio receivers. Although the Doppler shift may not seem to place amplitude modulation onto the received signal, it effectively does so. The shifted and non-shifted signals interact, and effectively modulate the received signal at the so-called "beat" frequency. In other words, if the shifted signal is changed by 10Hz, the received signal contains amplitude modulation at 10Hz. The frequency shift will be quite small, giving an output frequency from the demodulator that is in the sub-audio or low audio frequency range.

The output level from the demodulator will often be quite low, and an amplifier is therefore used to substantially boost the signal. The amplified signal is used to trigger a monostable which controls a relay. The relay closes for a second or so once the unit has been activated, and this is more than enough time to reliably trigger the main alarm.

The Circuit

The circuit diagram for the ultrasonic transmitter appears in Figure 2.26. This is basically just a 555 astable which directly drives the ultrasonic transducer (LS1). VR1 enables the output frequency to be trimmed to the frequency at which the transducers provide optimum results.

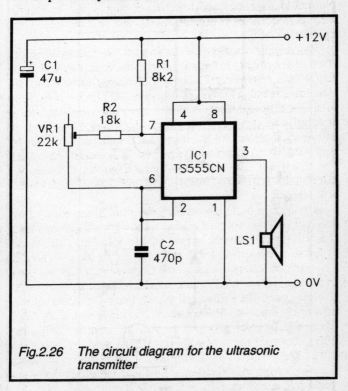

Fig.2.26   The circuit diagram for the ultrasonic transmitter

Figure 2.27 shows the circuit diagram for the receiver. The receiving transducer (Mic1) is connected to the input of a straightforward common emitter amplifier which utilizes TR1. C4 couples the output from this stage to a second common emitter amplifier which is based on TR2. The output from the collector of TR2 is coupled by C5 to a conventional half wave rectifier and smoothing circuit which utilizes D1 and D2.

125

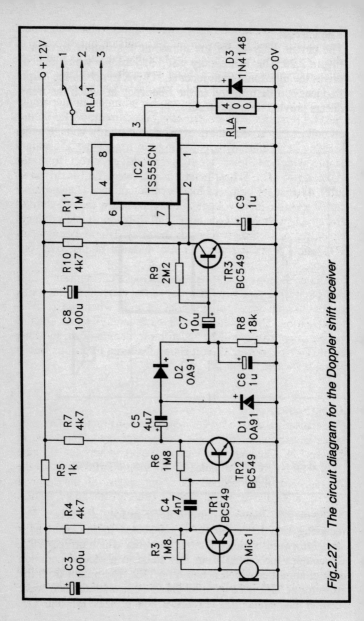

Fig.2.27   The circuit diagram for the Doppler shift receiver

126

Smoothing capacitor C6 has a much higher value than would normally be used in this form of demodulator, but the value of this component has to reflect the fact that the carrier and modulation frequencies are both much lower than normal.

The low frequency modulation signal is coupled by C7 to the base of TR3, which operates as another common emitter amplifier. R9 provides only a small base bias current to TR3 so that its collector is at something over half the supply voltage under standby conditions. This is too high to trigger the 555 monostable which is based on IC2, and driven direct from the collector of TR3. When the unit is activated, TR3 is driven so strongly that its output signal becomes clipped. On negative half cycles the input voltage to IC2 falls below the one third of the supply voltage trigger level, and the monostable produces an output pulse that switches on the relay. Timing components R11 and C9 set the output pulse duration at just over one second.

Under standby conditions the current consumption of the full circuit is about 5 milliamps, and the consumption rises by about 30 milliamps for the brief periods when the relay is switched on. This could be provided by batteries, but a mains power supply unit will be much more economic in the long term. The low power 12 volt supply featured in chapter one is suitable for this circuit.

Construction

The transmitter and receiver circuits are constructed on a single piece of stripboard using the component layout provided in Figure 2.28. The underside view of the board appears in Figure 2.29. The board has 46 holes by 20 copper strips. Parts of the board, particularly around the input stages of the receiver circuit, are quite cramped. Take extra care to guard against accidental short circuits when constructing this board.

The notes on the relay used in the window alarm also apply to the relay in this project. D1 and D2 are germanium diodes, and these are less hardy than silicon types such as the 1N4148 used for D3. It is not essential to use a heat-shunt on each lead as it is soldered into place, but the bit of the iron should not be applied to each joint for any longer than is really necessary.

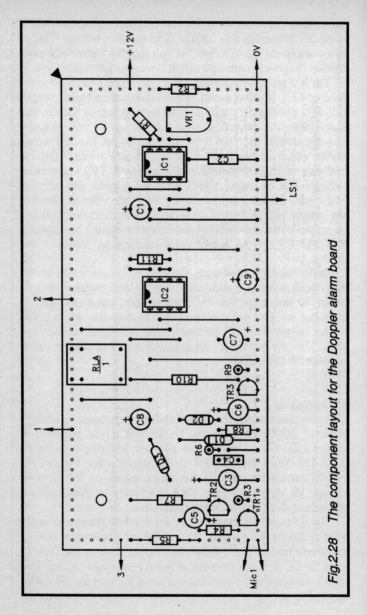

Fig.2.28   The component layout for the Doppler alarm board

128

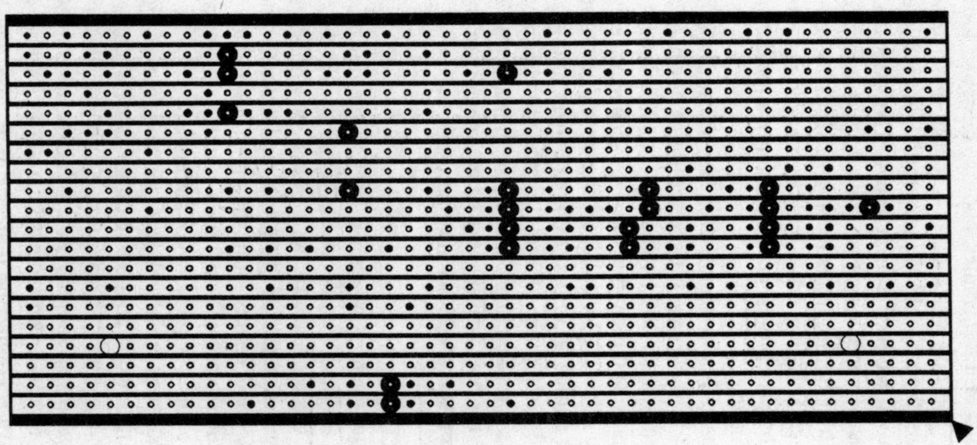

Fig.2.29   The underside view of the Doppler alarm board

As pointed out previously, ultrasonic transducers are normally sold as matched pairs. Sometimes the two units are identical, but usually they consist of one transducer designed for optimum results as a transmitter, and one designed for use as a microphone. The unit will almost certainly work reasonably well if you get them the wrong way round, but it is clearly better if they are fitted the right way round. The markings on the components usually make it clear as to which is which (e.g. "T40-16" on the transmitting transducer, and "R40-16" on the receiving transducer). If they have the same markings, or no markings at all, they are almost certainly identical, and can be used either way round.

Ultrasonic transducers invariably lack any form of built-in mounting bracket. The easiest way of mounting them on the front panel of the case is to drill two pairs of small holes to take their connecting pins, and then glue them in place using a good quality gap-filling adhesive. A quick setting epoxy adhesive is probably the best choice. It is best to mount them at opposite ends of the panel, preferably around 150 to 200 millimetres apart, to minimise direct pickup between the transducers. The lead from Mic1 to the board must either be no longer than about 50 millimetres, or a screened lead must be used.

Adjustment and Use

If suitable test equipment is available, VR1 in the transmitter circuit is adjusted for the highest possible signal level at the collector of TR1 in the receiver. In the absence of suitable test equipment it is just a matter of using trial and error to find a setting that gives good results. Adjustment of VR1 does not seem to be particularly critical, and good results will probably be obtained over a fairly wide range of settings.

The unit should work quite well if it is aimed into a largely empty area, but this tends to give a rather narrow angle of coverage due to the highly directional nature of ultrasonic soundwaves. A maximum range of at least six to seven metres can normally be achieved. An increased area of coverage can often be achieved by aiming the unit at a wall, with the unit aimed at an angle of about 45 degrees to the wall rather than straight at it. The signal reflected from the wall helps to scatter the soundwaves so that they cover a larger area. It is a matter of experimenting a little in order to find a position and orientation for the unit that gives good coverage.

Components for Figures 2.26 and 2.27

Resistors (all 0.25 watt 5% carbon film)

R1	8k2
R2	18k
R3	1M8
R4	4k7
R5	1k
R6	1M8
R7	4k7
R8	18k
R9	2M2
R10	4k7
R11	1M

Potentiometer

VR1	22k min hor preset

Capacitors

C1	47µ 25V radial elect
C2	470p polystyrene
C3	100µ 16V radial elect
C4	4n7 polyester
C5	4µ7 50V radial elect
C6	1µ 50V radial elect
C7	10µ 25V radial elect
C8	100µ 16V radial elect
C9	1µ 50V radial elect

Semiconductors

IC1	TS555CN
IC2	TS555CN
TR1	BC549
TR2	BC549
TR3	BC549
D1	OA91
D2	OA91
D3	1N4148

RLA/1   12 volt 400R coil, single changeover contact (see text)

Mic1/LS1   40kHz ultrasonic transducers (see text)

Case, 0.1 inch pitch stripboard measuring 46 holes by 20 copper strips, 8-pin DIL holder (2 off), wire, solder, etc.

Broken IR Beam Sensor

The most simple form of broken beam detector consists of an ordinary torch bulb plus a reflector or lens to provide a fairly narrow beam of light. The beam of light is shone onto some form of photo-cell, which can be something as basic as a cadmium sulphide photo-resistor. When the beam of light is broken, usually by someone passing through it, the photocell receives a much lower light level, and its resistance increases. This is detected by a simple circuit which activates a relay. The relay in turn activates an alarm (or whatever).

This type of broken beam detector is very simple, but it has the disadvantage that it can be blocked by high ambient light levels. Also, the beam of light is easily detected, which is obviously a major drawback in security applications. A system based on a modulated infra-red beam is better suited to most practical applications. The broken beam detector featured here uses a modulated infra-red beam, and Figure 2.30 shows the basic arrangement used.

The transmitter is very simple, and is little more than an audio oscillator operating at a frequency of a few kilohertz. The exact operating frequency of the oscillator is not particularly important, but it needs to be fairly high so that the receiver can easily distinguish between the pulse signal and any background noise. In particular, it needs to be able to readily detect the pulse signal while ignoring any 100Hz "hum" from mains powered lighting. On the other hand, the frequency must not be set so high that the l.e.d. and detector operate inefficiently. A frequency of a few kilohertz offers a good compromise.

The oscillator drives an infra-red l.e.d. via a buffer amplifier. The latter enables the l.e.d. to be driven at a high current, but the signal from the l.e.d. is still fairly weak. It is for this

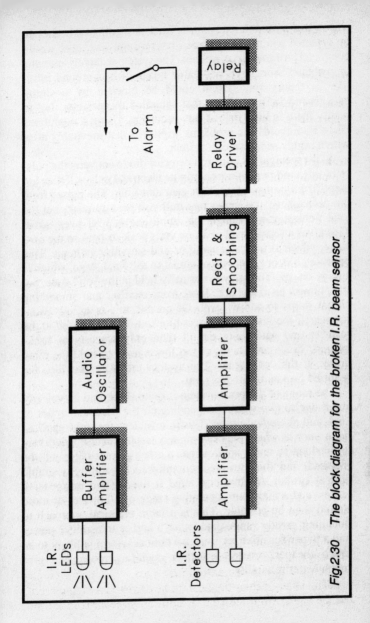

Fig.2.30   The block diagram for the broken I.R. beam sensor

reason that a modulated beam is used. A modulated beam can be detected against an infra-red background level that would completely swamp a d.c. system. The system is largely immune to problems from high but stable levels of background infra-red. In theory the system could be blocked by a strong background infra-red level that saturated the detector, but in reality there is little risk of this occurring. Using a modulated beam also avoids the problems with drift that inevitably arise with a highly sensitive d.c. system.

At the receiver an infra-red detector diode converts the pulses of infra-red radiation into minute electrical pulses. These are amplified by a two-stage high gain amplifier. The pulses from the detector may be under one millivolt peak-to-peak, but the total voltage gain through the amplifiers is well over 80dB. This gives a signal level of a few volts peak-to-peak to the next stage, which is a simple rectifier and smoothing circuit. This produces a strong d.c. output signal to the final stage, which is a relay driver. The relay is normally held in the "off" state, but it is turned on if the d.c. level from rectifier and smoothing circuit drops to a low level. Of course, this is exactly what happens if the infra-red beam is blocked. The signal fed to the rectifier and smoothing circuit then only consists of background "hiss", and this is at too low a level to hold the relay driver in the "off" state. The system therefore provides the required broken beam detection.

The range of the basic system is quite short, and is typically about one to two metres, depending on the particular types of l.e.d. and photodiode used. This is sufficient for some applications, such as where the beam merely has to traverse a doorway or corridor. In many applications a much greater range will be required, and this can be accomplished by adding a simple optical system. All that is needed is one or two inexpensive lenses, and a maximum operating range of 10 metres or more should then be possible. This is a more practical approach to obtaining greater range than using a higher transmitter power and a hyper-sensitive receiver. An optical system is likely to be much cheaper, provide a greater operating range, and give much better reliability.

134

Twin Beams

Although a broken infra-red beam detector is usually very reliable, there is a potential flaw in a system of this type. The problem is simply that the effective beam width of the system is very narrow. If the system includes one or two lenses, the effective beam width is round 25 to 50 millimetres. If no lens system is used, other than any built-in lenses the l.e.d. and photodiode may have, the effective beam width is only a few millimetres. This can result in false alarms due to moths or other insects flying through the beam.

There are various approaches to combatting this problem, but the twin beam system is probably the most effective. Some systems have two transmitters and two receivers operating as what are virtually independent broken beam systems. In this case the simpler option is used, with two l.e.d.s being used at the transmitter, and two infra-red detectors at the receiver. Provided the system is not used over an excessive range, a link between one l.e.d. and one infra-red detector will be sufficient to prevent the receiver from being activated.

The two beams are normally positioned quite close together. They would typically be about 300 to 400 millimetres apart, and one above the other. The system is arranged so that the relay is only activated if both beams are broken simultaneously. Someone passing through the beams will break both of them at the same time, and will activate the system. An insect will only break one beam, or will break both beams at separate times. Either way, an insect will fail to trigger the unit and produce a false alarm.

Transmitter

The circuit diagram for the transmitter appears in Figure 2.31. This is basically just a 555 timer used in the standard astable (oscillator) mode. It provides a roughly squarewave output signal at pin 3. The operating frequency is set at approximately 6.6kHz by timing components R1, R2, and C2. TR1 is the buffer amplifier, and this is a straightforward emitter follower stage. It drives the infra-red l.e.d.s (D1 and D2) via separate current limiting resistors (R3 and R4). The 555 can actually provide quite high output currents, but the total "on" current for

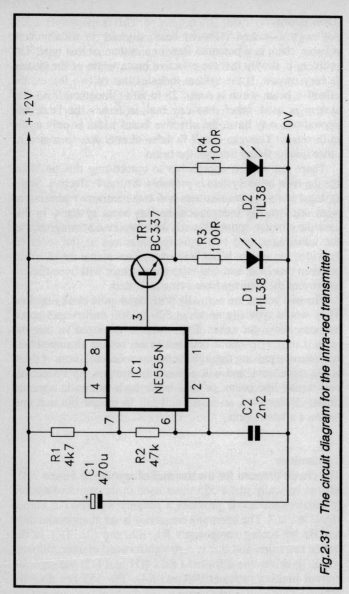

Fig.2.31   The circuit diagram for the infra-red transmitter

the two l.e.d.s is about 200 milliamps. This is more than a 555 can handle reliably. The l.e.d.s are switched off for about 50 percent of the time, so the average current is approximately 50 milliamps per l.e.d. This is the maximum average current rating for most 5 millimetre diameter infra-red l.e.d.s.

The current consumption of the entire circuit is around 108 milliamps. Powering the unit from batteries is not very practical, and there is little choice but to use a mains power supply unit. The higher power supply featured in chapter one is suitable for this project.

Construction

Details of the stripboard layout for the infra-red transmitter appear in Figure 2.32. The underside view of the board is shown in Figure 2.33. The board measures 24 holes by 15 copper strips.

A TIL38 is specified for D1, but this can be any 5 millimetre diameter infra-red l.e.d. Components of this type are not always given type numbers in component catalogues. They often seem to be described simply as "5mm infra-red l.e.d.s", or "5mm remote control infra-red l.e.d.s". Any 5 millimetre diameter infra-red l.e.d. of the type sold for use in remote control systems should work well in this circuit. In some cases you may have a choice of wide or narrow beam l.e.d.s. Assuming that you are not going to use a separate optical system, the narrow beam type will give a somewhat greater operating range. A wide beam l.e.d. is probably the better choice if you are going to use the transmitter with a lens.

Components for Figure 2.31

Resistors (0.25 watt 5% carbon film except where noted)
R1   4k7
R2   47k
R3   100R 1 watt
R4   100R 1 watt

Capacitors
C1   470µ 10V elect
C2   2n2 polyester

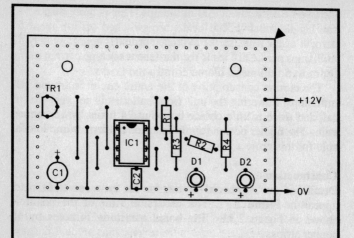

Fig.2.32 The component layout for the infra-red transmitter

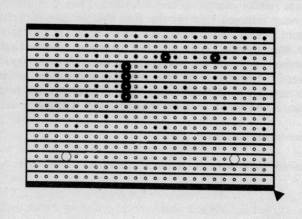

Fig.2.33 The underside of the infra-red transmitter board

138

Semiconductors

IC1	NE555N
D1	TIL38 or similar (see text)
D1	TIL38 or similar (see text)
TR1	BC337

Miscellaneous

Case, 0.1 inch pitch stripboard having 24 holes by 15 copper strips, 8-pin DIL IC holder, 5mm l.e.d. holders, wire, solder, etc.

Receiver Circuit

Figure 2.34 shows the circuit diagram for the receiver. D1 and D2 are the infra-red detector diodes, and they are large area photodiodes of the type sold for use in infra-red remote control systems. D1 and D2 are used in the reverse bias mode. Like any semiconductor diodes, they have a very high resistance when reverse biased, and pass only minute leakage currents. The pulses of infra-red from the transmitter produce a significant increase in the leakage level of D1 and D2, and produce small voltage pulses at the junction of R1, D1, and D2.

The alternative operating mode for a photodiode is the voltaic mode. In this mode it does not have the bias resistor (R1), and it operates rather like a solar cell, generating small voltages from the infra-red pulses. The voltaic mode tends to give lower sensitivity than the reverse biased mode, and it is therefore the latter that is used in this circuit. There is no need for a mixer circuit to combine the outputs of D1 and D2. With the reverse bias mode of operation it is acceptable to add any number of diodes in parallel.

TR1 and TR2 provide the two stages of amplification, and these are both common emitter amplifiers. The values of coupling capacitors C2 and C4 have been made quite low so that the amplifier has a very poor low frequency response. This does not significantly reduce the sensitivity of the circuit to the 6.6kHz signal from the transmitter, but it does considerably reduce the sensitivity to 100Hz mains "hum". C3 and C5 provide high frequency roll-off which aids good stability.

C6 couples the output from TR2 to a simple half-wave rectifier and smoothing circuit based on D3 and D4. The decay

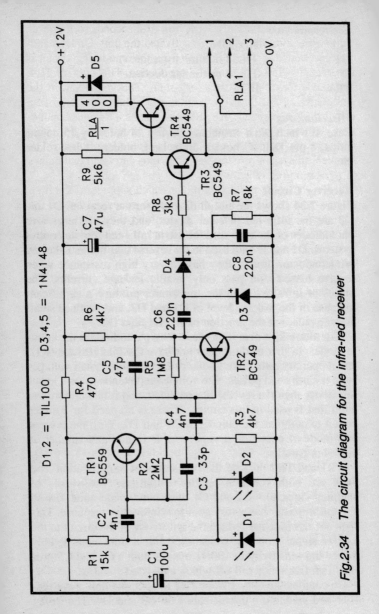

D1,2 = TIL100   D3,4,5 = 1N4148

Fig.2.34   The circuit diagram for the infra-red receiver

140

time of the circuit is only a fraction of a second, so that even briefly breaking the beam will activated the unit. Under stand-by conditions the output voltage from the smoothing circuit is sufficient to bias TR3 hard into conduction. This cuts off TR4, and holds the relay in the "off" state. The voltage from the smoothing circuit quickly subsides when the beam is broken, causing TR3 to switch off. R9 then biases TR4 into conduction, and the relay is switched on. The circuit does not latch, and once the beam is restored, the relay switches off again. The main alarm system provides latching, plus entry and exit delays or remote on/off switching.

D5 is the usual protection diode which suppresses the high reverse voltage that would otherwise be generated across the relay coil as it switched off. It is worth repeating the warning that semiconductors are very intolerant of high voltages, and this reverse voltage could easily damage the semiconductors in the circuit if it was not suppressed.

The current consumption of the circuit is typically about 2.8 milliamps under standby conditions. It is substantially higher than this when the relay switches on, and the exact current consumption depends on the resistance of the relay used. The current consumption is typically around 33 milliamps with the relay activated. Although the standby current consumption is low enough to permit the use of a high capacity battery supply, and mains power supply unit is a more practical choice. The low power circuit featured in chapter one is suitable for use with this circuit.

Construction
Refer to Figure 2.35 for the component layout of the stripboard panel. The underside view of the board appears in Figure 2.36. The board has 32 holes by 20 copper strips. Construction of the board is largely straightforward, but be careful not to omit any of the link wires. The notes on the relay used in the window alarm apply equally to the relay used in this project.

The TIL100 is specified for D1 and D2, but any vaguely similar infra-red photodiode should work just as well. Some component catalogues do not seem to list devices of this type under specific type numbers, but instead simply describe them as something like an "infra-red photodiode". Any large photo-

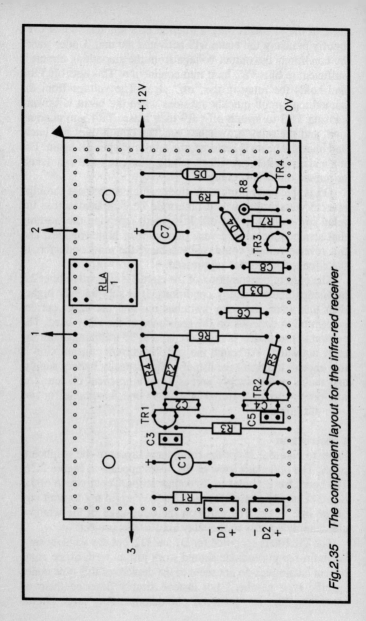

Fig.2.35   The component layout for the infra-red receiver

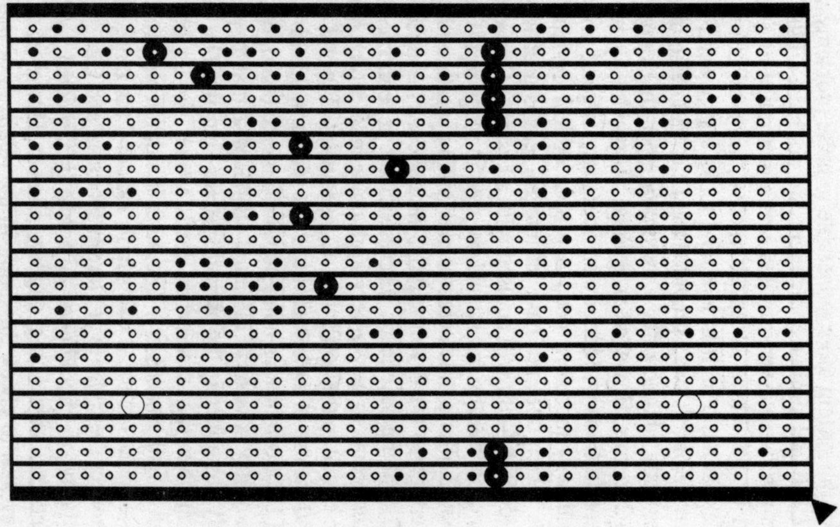

Fig.2.36   The underside of the infra-red receiver board

diode of this general type should work well in this circuit. Small photodiodes should work in this circuit, but would probably give only a very short operating range. It is preferable to use a type having a built-in filter that gives low sensitivity to visible light (a so-called "daylight" filter). However, devices that do not have a built-in filter will work in this circuit, but might make the system more vulnerable to noise problems.

The TIL100 and similar components do not have a built-in lens. This results in a very limited maximum range of about one metre or so. There is an alternative form of infra-red photodiode that has a built-in lens, and looks very much like a l.e.d. A device of this type, provided the l.e.d. and detector are aligned correctly, should offer a maximum operating range of more than 2 metres. However, as pointed out previously, many practical applications will require an operating range of several metres, and will therefore need a proper optical system. A photodiode which does not have an integral lens is probably a better choice if the unit will be used with a system of lenses.

In theory, phototransistors could be used in place of D1 and D2, and would offer a much greater maximum operating range. The emitters go to the 0 volt supply, the collectors connect to R1 and C2, and the base leads (if present) left unconnected. In practice this seems to give a very high noise level which tends to hold the circuit in the "off" state. Consequently, I would only recommend the use of a photodiode as the sensor in this circuit.

D1 and D2 are shown as being mounted on the board, but in practice they may have to be mounted off-board so that they can be correctly positioned in the optical system. They must be hard wired to the board via screened leads which should be no longer than is really necessary. The outer braiding connects the anode (–) terminals to the 0 volt supply rail, and the inner conductors connect the cathode (+) terminals to R1 and C2.

The polarity of photodiodes is normally indicated by the cathode leadout wire being slightly shorter. However, it is probably as well to check this point in the retailer's or manufacturer's data for the particular type of component you use. For the TIL100 and similar diodes the sensitive surface is the large one opposite the side which carries the type number, etc. For other types which do not have a built-in lens it would be advisable to check the retailer's or manufacturer's data, since these diodes come in a variety of shapes and sizes.

If you decide to use your own circuit board design, bear in mind that this circuit has a substantial amount of voltage gain and that the input and output of the two stage amplifier are in-phase. The high frequency roll-off provided by C3 and C5 minimise problems with stray feedback, but does not totally avoid them. A sensible layout must be used or the amplifier will become unstable, and may hold the relay in the "off" state when the beams are broken. In particular, keep the wiring around D1 and D2 well away from the wiring to the collector of TR2. Note that the stripboard layout provided here has one or two link-wires and breaks in the copper strips that serve no obvious purpose. These are used to minimise stray feedback and the risk of instability.

Components for Figure 2.34

Resistors (all 0.25 watt 5% carbon film)

R1	15k
R2	2M2
R3	4k7
R4	470R
R5	1M8
R6	4k7
R7	18k
R8	3k9
R9	5k6

Capacitors

C1	100µ 16V elect
C2	4n7 polyester
C3	33p ceramic
C4	4n7 polyester
C5	47p ceramic
C6	220n polyester
C7	47µ 25V radial elect
C8	220n polyester

145

Semiconductors

D1	TIL100 or similar (see text)
D2	TIL100 or similar (see text)
D3	1N4148
D4	1N4148
D5	1N4148
TR1	BC559
TR2	BC549
TR3	BC549
TR4	BC549

Miscellaneous

RLA/1	12 volt 400R coil, single changeover contact (see text)

Case, 0.1 inch pitch stripboard having 32 holes by 20 copper strips, wire, solder, etc.

Optical Systems

As pointed out previously, the range of the broken infra-red beam system can be greatly improved by adding a simple optical system. Although the basic system offers a maximum operating range of only about one to two metres, a simple optical system based on a couple of inexpensive lenses will increase this to at least 10 metres. In fact a single lens is sufficient if only a modest increase in range is needed. With one lens it should be possible to obtain a range of a little over three metres.

Figure 2.37 shows the way in which a single lens is used. The effect of the lens is to gather up the infra-red energy over a relatively large area, so that the amount of energy received is comparatively large. This energy is then concentrated onto the small sensitive area of the photodiode. This gives an output signal from the photodiode that is likely to be ten or more times higher than the signal obtained without the aid of a lens.

The lens must be a positive (convex) type, and in order to be reasonably effective it must have a diameter of 25 millimetres or more. The focal length is not of great importance in theory,

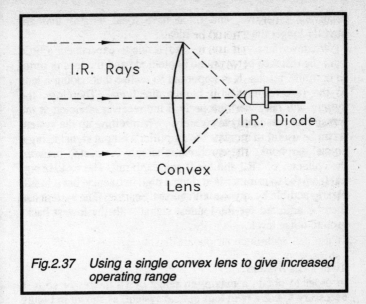

Fig.2.37 *Using a single convex lens to give increased operating range*

but in practice focal lengths of more than about 150 millimetres will be awkward to use due to the large distance required between the lens and the front of the photodiode. This distance must be approximately equal to the focal length of the lens. It is not advisable to use a lens having a very short focal length, since the positioning of the photodiode might then become very critical. Probably the best choice is a lens of about 25 to 50 millimetres in diameter, having a focal length of about 50 to 100 millimetres.

Some electronic component catalogues list a 30 millimetre diameter red tinted plastic lens (37 millimetres in diameter including the mounting rim) having a focal length of about 80 millimetres. This is specifically designed for use in applications of this type, and I have always obtained good results from this low cost lens. Bear in mind that high optical quality is of no importance in this application. In order to obtain good results it is merely necessary for the lens to roughly focus the infra-red signal onto the photodiode. Small magnifying glasses also seem to work well in this application, but they are likely to be

147

relatively expensive, and often have focal lengths that are slightly longer than would be ideal.

Whatever lens you use, it is advisable to experiment a little with the distance between the photodiode and the lens in order to optimise results. It is important to realise that adding a lens to the receiver makes it highly directional. Therefore, the system will only work properly if the receiver is aimed at the transmitter reasonably accurately. When setting up the system it can be useful to monitor the amplifier's output signal using a crystal earphone. The earphone is simply connected between the collector of TR2 and the 0 volt earth rail. The 6.6kHz signal from the transmitter is at quite a high frequency, but it is still clearly audible by anyone with normal hearing. The system can then be adjusted for the loudest signal with the lowest background noise level.

Twin Lens System

In order to obtain a maximum range of 10 metres or so it is necessary to use a twin lens optical system, as shown in Figure 2.38. This is very similar to the single lens method, but it also has a lens ahead of the l.e.d. at the transmitter. The two lenses do not have to be identical, but the lens at the transmitter needs to have broadly the same characteristics as the one at the receiver (i.e. a positive lens having a diameter of about 25 to 50 millimetres, and a focal length of about 50 to 100 millimetres).

The effect of the lens is to focus the infra-red from the l.e.d. into a tight beam that diverges very gradually. Because the beam does not spread very much over a distance of a few metres, the intensity remains high even several metres away from the transmitter. The focusing of the beam will not be perfect of course, and the beam does gradually weaken as the range of the system is increased. A maximum range of at least 10 metres should be possible though, and a range as great as 20 metres might be possible if the optics are set up and aligned very accurately.

There is a slight problem with this system in that it renders both the transmitter and the receiver highly directional. This makes it difficult to get everything accurately set up, but a long

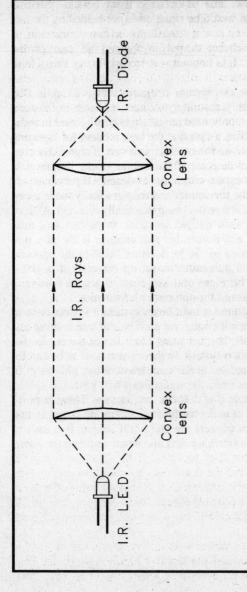

I.R. Diode

Convex Lens

I.R. Rays

Convex Lens

I.R. L.E.D.

Fig.2.38   Using two lenses to provide greatly increased range

149

operating range will only be obtained if the optical system is quite accurately aligned. The situation is not helped by the fact that the infra-red l.e.d. only transmits infra-red radiation. It produces no significant output in the visible part of the spectrum, and its "light" output is therefore totally invisible to a human observer.

In order to get the system operating correctly it is first necessary to get the transmitter to direct its beam in the right direction. The l.e.d. only needs to be slightly off-centre in order to misdirect the beam. I find that the best method for adjusting the transmitter is to use the receiver as a sort of signal detector. It works best as a detector if the output of the amplifier is monitored using a crystal earphone, as described previously. If you start close to the transmitter and then gradually move away, you can determine where the beam is actually directed. A bit of trial and error is then needed in order to correct any mis-alignment of the l.e.d. Remember that an error in the direction of the beam is caused by the l.e.d. being "out" in the opposite direction. Once the transmitter is set up correctly it is just a matter of using a bit more trial and error to get the receiver's optical system adjusted for optimum performance.

Of course, if you use a twin beam system it is necessary to use an identical optical system for each pair of transmitting and receiving photocells. In other words, four lenses are needed for a twin lens twin beam system. In theory you have to be careful not to aim both receivers at the same transmitting photocell. In practice the beams from the transmitter will probably spread sufficiently to ensure that this can not happen. There is probably a greater risk of using too great an operating range, so that blocking one beam triggers the alarm. Of course, it is easy to check this point by blocking first one beam and then the other.